ROYAL COLLEGE
OF SURGEONS
OF ENGLAND

Medical Museums

Past, Present, Future

Edited by
Samuel JMM Alberti and Elizabeth Hallam

Medical Museums: Past, Present, Future

First edition printed in 2013 in the United Kingdom.

British Library Cataloguing in Publication Data. A catalogue record for this book is available from the British Library.

ISBN 978-1-904096-21-4

While every effort has been made to ensure the accuracy of the information contained in this publication, no guarantee can be given that all errors and omissions have been excluded. No responsibility for loss occasioned to any person acting or refraining from action as a result of the material in this publication can be accepted by The Royal College of Surgeons of England or the contributors.

Published by The Royal College of Surgeons of England
35–43 Lincoln's Inn Fields
London WC2A 3PE
www.rcseng.ac.uk

Printed in the United Kingdom by Advent Colour Ltd.
This work is printed on FSC accredited paper.

EDIT, DESIGN AND TYPESET
Adam Brownsell, Vivienne Button and Matthew Whitaker at RCS Publishing

COVER DESIGN
Angelo Vieira

COVER IMAGES
John Carr

Contents

Foreword

Sir Barry Jackson
Chairman of the Board of Trustees of the Hunterian Collection

In the first decades of the twenty-first century the public interest in medicine has never been greater. Witness the almost daily articles in newspapers and magazines and the numerous television programmes, both serious and sensational. Another reflection of this deep-rooted interest is the growing audience for medical museums and their diverse collections. It is fitting, therefore, that on the occasion of the bicentenary of the opening of the world-famous Hunterian Museum within the Royal College of Surgeons of England that this lavishly illustrated, scholarly but eminently readable book is published.

Contained within its pages are fascinating accounts written by curators, archivists, historians and researchers relating to museums sited in Europe and the United States of America. These institutions differ widely in their holdings and context, which makes each chapter distinctive. Few readers will be aware of all the museums that are discussed and many will likely be stimulated to widen their knowledge, perhaps even by visiting them. A clear vision emerges as to how the world of medical museums is adapting to meet the challenges of the future in a digital age.

Being an avid student of history while still a medical student I had read much about John Hunter, the eighteenth-century London surgeon and the so-called father of scientific surgery, before I qualified in 1963. This was also the year in which Hunter's rebuilt and refurbished museum reopened after sustaining serious war damage. I visited within weeks of the opening and have been a lifelong devotee of the Hunterian and other medical museums ever since. Fifty years later, and now chairman of the board responsible to the nation for the care and safe-keeping of Hunter's original collection, it is with delight that I commend this volume, which I know will give much pleasure to all who read it.

Acknowledgements

At the Royal College of Surgeons we are grateful to Adam Brownsell, Vivienne Button, Jane Hughes, Sir Barry Jackson, Professor Vishy Mahadevan, Angelo Vieira and Matt Whitaker. At the University of Aberdeen, we thank Neil Curtis; the staff in Anatomy, especially Margaret Moir, Dr Ian Stewart and Dr Peter Johnston in Pathology.

Elsewhere we would like to thank Fay Bound Alberti of Queen Mary University of London, Ian Maclachlan at the University of Oxford, Lynn Schwartz, formerly of Kings' College London, Jenny Whitebread and Michael Whitebread at Adam,Rouilly, and for information about the Semmelweis Museum we are very grateful to Benedek Varga, Director General of the Semmelweis Museum, Library and Archives of the History of Medicine, Budapest.

We are indebted to all the institutions and photographers who generously let us use their photographs, including Joanna Ebenstein, John McIntosh and Tanya Marcuse. We have named the makers and artists where known but we would also like to thank the many anonymous craftspeople whose names are lost to history. We have tried to ensure credit is afforded to all copyright holders, please let us know if we have omitted any.

Finally, we could not have realised this project without the generous support of the Board of Trustees of the Hunterian Collection and the Trustees of the Frances and Augustus Newman Foundation.

Bodies in Museums

Elizabeth Hallam and Samuel JMM Alberti

Museums are full of bodies. Bodies of visitors gaze at bodies of knowledge writ large on display. But there is a particular genre of collections that has an unusual concentration of bodies: medical museums. It is these institutions that we explore throughout this volume, in Europe and the United States. Often difficult to find, these fascinating places present rare and sometimes challenging exhibitions of bodies that provoke different reactions. Entering them is not always comfortable, for they offer insights inside bodies and in doing so they invite viewers to reflect on themselves.

Bodies in medical museums take many varied and changing forms. Innumerable preserved dead bodies – or rather, body parts – are displayed on gallery shelves or kept in storerooms. Further countless living bodies have worked with these physical remains, to craft and preserve them, in addition to creating vast ranges of images, devices and instruments that populate museums of medicine. Human bodies in museums are also persons, whether alive or deceased. Preserved remains were derived from once living people, and these continue to have post-mortem social lives – they are perceived to take on roles, and have capacities to influence and affect the people who engage with them. The life of medical museums is propelled by yet more bodies: those of countless visitors who enter exhibitions dedicated to probing human medical endeavour.

This volume, rather than aiming to be encyclopaedic, explores a selection of collections, held largely by educational institutions, to illustrate the many forms taken by medical museums – from seldom-seen collections in cupboards to thriving international displays of science and technology. This diversity is mirrored by the differing perspectives taken by our authors, who include curators, historians, artists and anthropologists – some medically trained, most not. We hope this book might inspire readers to seek out further museums elsewhere.

Focusing on bodies, along with instruments and other artefacts used in the pursuit of wellbeing, this introduction outlines medical museums in historical and contemporary perspectives, highlighting their scope and dynamic capacity for change. Museums, and the bodies within them, shape and are shaped by their never-static social and cultural settings. Our aim is to provide historical context for the chapters that follow, as authors explore the past, present and future of medical museums.

FIGURE 1
Ole Worm's museum in Copenhagen: from *Museum Wormianum* (1655). Wellcome Library, London.

WONDER AND BEAUTY

Bodies featured in early modern collections, which embraced a staggering variety of items, whether considered natural or artificial, or a striking fusion of both. Amassing in *Wunderkammern* (chambers of wonder) and cabinets of curiosities (see Schnalke in this volume), was a profusion of things: plants, preserved parts of animals, stones, metals, artefacts, human bodies (and parts thereof) – either in the flesh or in fabricated versions, such as automata. Some relics of saints were incorporated into such cabinets (having survived from medieval collections that inspired awe and devotion at sacred sites). Among further human remains that were highly prized for their perceived rarity and strangeness were mummified heads, foetuses with many limbs and unusual stones from kidneys (Figure 1). These collecting practices – undertaken during the sixteenth and seventeenth centuries by merchants, lawyers and scholars as well as physicians and apothecaries – produced abundant assemblages that provoked amazement at God's creation. But collections were also for study, the exploration of materials' natural properties, and the formation of social connections in which the collector's own identity was shaped. Collecting of this sort was regarded as crucial in the forging of medical knowledge; it also reinforced the social status of medical practitioners within their localities and in wider networks of scholars and gentleman travellers.

While bodies preserved in these early collections tended to be predominantly skeletal or dried, techniques for keeping fleshier parts were devised from the seventeenth century onwards. Anatomists used improved syringes for injecting fluids into blood vessels, and they immersed dissected parts in spirit (alcohol) so that they would resist decay for years, suspended in glass jars. Crafting these preparations was a skill cultivated though observation, experiments and work with the hands. Furthermore, eighteenth-century anatomists – in Leiden for instance – made preparations from deceased bodies with a view to prevalent notions of acceptability and beauty (see Hendriksen, Huistra and Knoeff in this volume). Nevertheless, the spectrum of reactions to even the most finely wrought preparation could still include disgust and horror, depending on viewer and context.

In London, William Hunter, at his Great Windmill Street anatomy school and residence, referred to particular injected parts as 'beautiful', even as he determined to avoid idealising the body in his work and instead provide illustrations and plaster casts bearing a 'very perfect likeness' to human anatomy. Hunter rejected wax anatomical models with what he saw as 'unnatural colours', and yet in different settings in Continental Europe, such waxes were employed extensively to educate both lay and medical audiences (see Maerker, and Ebenstein, in this volume).[1] Female models with idealised bodies, or anatomical Venuses, which could be taken apart, were 'powerful magnet[s]' for exhibition visitors in Florence during the late 1700s, and have since attracted much analysis by historians of art, medicine and gender.[2]

The form, presentation and appreciation of bodies in museums, whether preserved or fabricated (or mixtures of both), were shaped by aesthetic evaluations, which change according to historical period and place. In the early 1800s some Europeans saw in beauty a means to increase the educational potential of anatomical drawings and displays.[3] Cultural and social factors therefore shaped bodies in museums, even as far as the very kinds of bodies that it was possible to collect and exhibit. These factors were both local and global, especially given eighteenth-century exploration, and the expansion of trade and colonial territories. William Hunter's extensive museum, and that of his brother, John (see Alberti in this volume), were made possible by transactions both nearby and overseas where their dealers, agents and former students sourced desirable artefacts and materials. Human remains, the bodies of mammals, birds, reptiles, fish, insects, and plants, were acquired in this way (Figure 2). Even the body of the esteemed anatomist – whose knowledge and reputation was boosted by an impressive museum – became collectable: a plaster-cast copy of William Hunter's death mask is held at the University of Glasgow to which he bequeathed the contents of his museum. Currently much of this collection is exhibited for the public at the university's Hunterian Museum, and Museum of Anatomy.

FIGURE 2
The foetus of a horse, with its membranes, from John Hunter's 18th-century comparative anatomy collection.
Hunterian Museum at the Royal College of Surgeons.

'ABNORMALITY' AND DISEASE

The macabre seeds sewn in the Enlightenment bore their morbid fruit in the Victorian era. Medical collections founded in the late eighteenth and nineteenth centuries were at the intersection of a number of cultural and scientific currents: the development of pathology and comparative anatomy as disciplines, the formalisation of medical education, European colonial expansion, and the spread of popular shows and exhibitions. This combination generated tens of thousands of specimens (as preserved body parts were termed) for generations of visitors. In the process, scientists' and medical practitioners' definitions of what was 'normal' or 'abnormal' were made visible, thereby shaping perceptions of social and cultural as well as bodily differences.

Perceived educational need was a significant driver for the endurance and growth of medical collections. Anatomy was a central part of medical education and qualifications, and medical teachers relied on dissecting deceased bodies as well as museum collections of skilfully prepared specimens. Under the 1832 Anatomy Act in the UK, those bodies unclaimed by relatives (in practice, those of the very poor) could be used by licensed anatomists in their teaching, but they had to be given appropriate burial within a specified period of time. Selected parts of bodies retained as specimens in museums were displayed for considerably longer.

Towards the end of the nineteenth century the student body using medical collections encompassed women as well as men, as women began to enter the medical profession (Figure 3).

Arguments against women studying medicine had been informed by cultural assumptions about women's capacities and roles. Dominant views of respectable femininity and modesty jarred with the possibility that young women would study in places where the naked bodies of the dead were exposed, especially dissecting rooms and museums. Despite rising numbers of trained women, and their long-standing contributions to the work of healing and scientific investigation, many positions of authority in medicine, as in museums, were occupied by men well into the twentieth century, as chapters in this book indicate.

Within medical museums both male and female bodies were opened to in-depth exploration. What were identified as pathological specimens were used to show students and clinicians rare diseases that they would not otherwise encounter in living patients or dissections. This use of medical collections – for vivid and tangible demonstration of what could go wrong with the body, as well as what a healthy body should look like – was a key function. It also accounted for their size. For every 'normal' organ in a collection there were countless variations illustrating different diseases and afflictions, growth or shrinkage. Pathologists collected tens of thousands of specimens from their private patients, hospital wards and from colleagues further afield.[4]

But it wasn't only human bodies that stocked the shelves of medical museums. As they had been in cabinets of curiosities, zoological specimens were collected and displayed, usually as skeletons, the largest of which were hung from ceilings (Figure 4). Doctors learned about the function of the human body by comparing it to that of other vertebrates. Many nineteenth-century naturalists were medically trained, just as natural history collections were often to be found in medical schools and royal colleges (see Henry, and Alberti, in this volume).

One reason that comparative anatomy was so exciting to people during the decades around 1900 was the great diversity of species arriving in Europe and North America from the farthest

FIGURE 3
Dr Elizabeth McBean Ross (centre), one of the first women to graduate in medicine (1907) at the University of Glasgow, with her sister Dr Jane McBean Ross and her brother Dr James McBean Ross, around 1910.
© Tain & District Museum Trust; scran.ac.uk.

reaches of the globe. At the height of European imperialism institutional collections of all kinds swelled as colonial agents, scientists, doctors and soldiers sent back things they found (or bought, collected, hunted or killed) to their home city, museum or hospital. Among these items were some of the most troubling to be found in any museum: the remains of indigenous peoples (especially skulls), which formed the basis of massive physical anthropology collections. Identifying, measuring and classifying human physical differences in museums produced a 'typology of race' that was mapped onto humankind from (what was defined as) the 'civilised' (European) to the 'savage'.[5] Medical museums are, like the practices of medicine and science, far from neutral and innocent – they are thoroughly entangled in the conflicts, politics and material negotiations of life and death, from war to empire.

While the dead were collected, living people from across the globe were also displayed in shows and international fairs, a practice fraught with complicated power relationships. Medical museums were part of a network of sites for display that included popular commercial anatomy museums, and exhibitions of people advertised as 'freaks' or 'living curiosities' (Figure 5).[6] While the museums detailed in this volume developed within authoritative institutions, they did so alongside – but also in marked contrast to – commercial shows that they often considered suspect or socially damaging.

FROM MICRO TO DIGITAL

Since the 1920s and 1930s, when many medical museums were at the peak of their size (in terms of both visitors and specimens), shifts in medical curricula and wider social changes have contributed to their apparent decline. In 1950 the UK alone had some 80 medical collections active in teaching hospitals, universities and colleges, but few survive today. Along with undeniably massive losses, however, collections have been re-built, divided and relocated (see especially Hallam in this volume).

FIGURE 4 (BELOW)
The Royal College of Surgeons of
England Museum around 1910.
Suspended from the ceiling is
a sperm whale captured off the
coast of Tasmania in 1864.
Hunterian Museum at the Royal
College of Surgeons.

FIGURE 5 (OPPOSITE)
Show bill advertising Dr Kahn's
anatomical museum on Oxford
Street in London, mid-19th century.
Wellcome Library, London.

Rather than a straightforward slide into obsolescence, two themes are evident in the twentieth-century history of medical museums: developments in visual technologies for exploring and diagnosing bodies, and approaches to the acquisition and display of medical equipment and tools.

A prevalent practice within modern Western medicine, and therefore within medical collections, are techniques of observation, or close analysis. For centuries microscope slides have been collected, but from the late nineteenth century technical advances in histology – the microscopic study of cells – meant that cells on 3-by-1-inch glass sheets have been stored in their millions across medical establishments. These sometimes replaced but otherwise complemented gross specimens as

the main focus of attention in pathology, so extending medical collections of minute parts of bodies.

The microscope is only one ocular technology to have revolutionised medical education. As histopathology became a distinct enterprise a century ago, so too did radiology with the development of x-ray imaging from the 1890s onwards. But rather than eclipse the specimen as a way of viewing the interior of the body, x-ray images were often viewed and displayed in conjunction with museum pots (specimens in glass jars) as part of a multimedia mapping of the body (Figure 6). The Wellcome Museum of Medical Science (see Arnold and Chaplin in this volume) was especially important as a site for multimedia exhibits.

While body fragments were preserved for teaching and research, doctors and curators also began to retain medical instruments associated with prominent clinicians or important procedures (see Chelnick in this volume). Medicalised bodies were juxtaposed with the diagnostic, operative and post-mortem instruments applied to them.[7] Whether or not they were collected and displayed with bodies, what medical instruments share with human remains is the capacity to illicit embodied responses in viewers, as visitors imagine themselves with the disease or undergoing the procedure that such tools were made for.[8]

These medical history collections assumed a heritage function: rather than displaying tools in current use they preserved medical equipment deemed historically significant, often alongside libraries and archives (see Condrau, Edmonson, and Söderqvist and Pedersen, in this volume). Universities and medical schools cultivated museums for this purpose, expressing professional identity by forging a history in select artefacts as, for example, at the Melbourne Medical School's Medical History Museum.[9]

As the collecting of medical artefacts and technologies gained momentum into the twentieth century, institutions faced particular challenges. Just as the objects of medical investigation

315, OXFORD STREET, Near Regent Circus.

Madame Dimanche, 87 years of age, with a Horn on Her Fore head, measuring 12 inches in length, to be seen at the

ANATOMICAL MUSEUM, OF DOCTOR KAHN.

Never before Exhibited in London, now Open for the Inspection of the Public.

It consists of several hundred objects eminently interesting, one view even of which, is sufficient for those who are not Professors in medicine or surgery, to enable them to form an exact idea of the wonderful construction of the human body, justly entitled the master-piece of creation.

The objects in this Collection are partly natural, and partly most striking imitations by the first artists; such as Mr. Guy, sen., Dr. Anzoux, Dr. Certeaux, and Dr. Chalian, of Paris; and Mr. Paul Zeiller, of Munich.—It is, above all, in its Wax Imitations or preparations, the representation of nature is perfect.

PROGRAMME.
First Section.—A. Natural Objects.

1. Man, his primary form—from 14 days up to his perfect development
2. Several of the internal parts of man.
3. Preparations most skilfully injected.
4. A boy, embalmed, shewing the astonishing circulation of the blood.
5. Several parts of the human body; the nerves of which are prepared with much art.

Second Section.—B. Preparations in Wax.

1. Physiological anatomy—that is to say, all the parts of the human body, represented in their normal state.
2. A great number of pathological preparations, that is to say, parts of the human body, in the same state.
3. Diseases of the eyes, opthalmia.
4. Preparations relating to midwifery.
5. Deviations from nature, among which is found Madame Mianchi, 87 years of age, having a horn on the forehead, 12 inches long, of a natural size, and Monsieur Duval, with a Wen entirely surrounding his neck, 60 inches in diameter, he is still living at Paris.
6. The five senses of man capable of being demonstrated.
7. Microscopic embryology—the result of microscopic research

became smaller and more obscure with the growth of biomedicine (especially from the 1940s onwards), so too the tools used to study and diagnose became difficult to collect and interpret. Medical exploration has shifted to the genetic level, beyond that which can (in principle) be touched and displayed. As techniques for visualising the body have developed, especially with the use of computers and digital images taken at varying degrees of magnification, medical museums have engaged with them (see Söderqvist and Pedersen in this volume). New technologies provide as many opportunities as threats to medical collections and museums. The installation of computers in museum spaces once occupied by specimens can push the latter into storage, while those that survive on view can be examined in relation to digitally imaged bodies, such as those in the US National Library of Medicine's Visible Human Project, initiated in the 1990s.

REMAKING AND REMEMBERING

In medical education, specimens, models and instruments are used in association with emerging imaging technologies to train medical practitioners (Figure 7). It will be difficult for digital images to fully replace these longer-standing collections, especially given the importance placed on visual *and* tactile methods for learning to visualise and imagine three-dimensional anatomical structures and relationships in the human body. Indeed, the design of innovative pedagogical tools for learning anatomy develops through the use of existing collections.[10] And when fresh educational devices are introduced, medical museums shift accordingly. Some collections and displays are thus subject to remaking, which keeps them active and ensures their maintenance, while the status of others becomes precarious and can lead to their storage or disposal (see Åhrén in this volume).

Beyond medical education, preserved bodies and other holdings in medical museums continue to attract interest from artists and writers. In *Cast From Nature* (2011) Christine Borland painstakingly recast a nineteenth-century plaster cast of a

partially dissected anonymous man's body, a fibreglass version of which is displayed at the Royal College of Surgeons of Edinburgh (see Henry in this volume). Kathleen Jamie's writing engages with preserved museum bodies at the same college, describing experiences of sounds, smells and sights among gallery displays sealed from touch in glass jars.[11] Karen Ingham reconstructed and imagined the lives of individuals behind specimens at the Royal College of Surgeons of England in *Narrative Remains*, a project that vividly re-personalised the Hunterian Museum's collection.[12] In a film by the Brothers Quay, *The Phantom Museum: Random Forays into the Vaults of Sir Henry Wellcome's Medical Collection* (2003), on permanent screening in Wellcome Collection's *Medicine Man* exhibition, items held in storage, such as a prosthetic limb, move as though they have a life of their own (see Hicks, and Bud in this volume). Through sculpture, texts and film, then, the bodies and artefacts in medical museums become animated subjects rather than lifeless objects.

These innovative approaches and collaborations contribute to the ongoing rethinking of what preserved bodily remains are, as once living human beings, and how they should be treated. They coincide with public debate, in the UK and elsewhere, and with changes in law concerning how human remains are to be collected, retained and exhibited appropriately. The Human Tissue Act 2004 (England and Wales), for instance, regulates licensing for medical schools, research institutes, museums and galleries wishing to display human tissue less than 100 years old (although to date only 11 of 800 licences granted have been for public display). Given that bodies after death are often surrounded by highly emotive ritualised practices of disposal, deep concerns are raised when the deceased, or parts of them, are kept for what some might regard as inappropriate and disrespectful purposes. Medical curators, like anatomists, now seek to make explicit their respect and gratitude to donors – as at the Museum of Anatomy in Glasgow, where there are two books of remembrance dedicated to the people who bequeath their bodies for medical science.

One driver of legal changes in the UK in the twenty-first century was to remove impediments to the repatriation of human remains from museums to source communities, as the Native American Graves Protection and Repatriation Act (1990) in the US had encouraged the return of cultural artefacts and ancestral remains to First Nation groups. After decades of debate and pressure from claimant groups, museums began to return human remains acquired in colonial contexts to affiliated organisations, especially in Australia and New Zealand. Marischal Museum in Aberdeen (see Hallam in this volume), for example, returned nine *toi moko* – tattooed, preserved heads of Māori origin – to Te Papa Tongarewa Museum of New Zealand in 2007. With this return the *toi moko* were treated respectfully as ancestral remains, rather than as museum artefacts.[13]

Medical museums with public galleries have scope for critical reflection on the context, provenance and previous uses of collections, and current curatorial practices aim to deal with the sometimes troubled history of collecting and exhibiting in sensitive and ethically informed ways. These museums now also demonstrate their relevance to medicine today. Emphasis is on stimulating visitors' interest and generating questions. At the Semmelweis Museum in Budapest, for example, exhibitions deliberately present several different (sometimes conflicting) interpretations of medical issues to provide visitors with multiple views of body conditions, afflictions, and treatments (Figure 8).

The museums and collections in this book mainly comprise bodies and artefacts forged through the development of biomedicine in Europe and the US, yet this forging has involved interactions with non-Western material cultures. So within some collections there is potential to explore radically different perceptions and therapeutic treatments of bodies (see Bud in this volume). Although in medical museums where non-Western artefacts were collected in the late-nineteenth and early-twentieth century, items have often been separated off to form anthropological museums (see Hallam in this volume).

Medical collections and museums are now also remade and reconstituted through the internet and social media, which link collections to recent developments in science and society (see Hicks, and Bud, in this volume). Expanding their audiences to remote users worldwide, for instance, museums are launching freely searchable websites with thousands of digital images, including those of preserved human and animal bodies. Rather than walking through galleries, viewers can navigate through collections according to their interests.

LOOKING FORWARD

On-site visitors nevertheless remain at the heart of museum practice. Medical professionals attend not only as part of their training but also to celebrate the heritage of their profession. Artists marvel at the form of the body, inside and out; those with an eye for history enjoy a cultural perspective. Members of thriving young subcultures thrill at what they see as the macabre, while researchers find source material for their investigations of pressing issues past and present. For many reasons there is continued public interest in displays of medical technology and human remains. Millions have flocked to Gunther von Hagens' *Body Worlds* exhibition and new sites such as Wellcome Collection report unprecedented numbers of visitors (see Arnold and Chaplin in this volume). With an eye on anatomy and pathology curricula, and through collaboration with faculty, collections are being redeployed for medical education.

However, the challenges for (often under-funded) medical museums concerned with the human body are great as biomedicine now deals in increasingly complex technology with global reach; as medical and surgical interventions become ever-more routine; as research into fatal diseases deepens; as industries for medicinal products and devices expand; and as people engage with very different kinds of diagnostic and

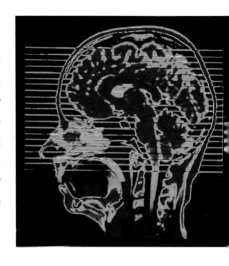

FIGURE 7
MRI scan of the head showing the brain as well as nasal and oral structures. This medical imaging technology has been developed in Britain since the early 1960s. Wellcome Library, London.

FIGURE 8
*Heart Beat: Past and Present of
Cardiology.* Temporary exhibition
at Semmelweis Museum of
Medical History, Budapest, in
2012. Curated by Dr Katalin Szabó
and Benedek Varga, and designed
by Heonlab. Here exhibition
design is intended to be a form of
contemporary art to make museum
communication more effective.
Photograph by Eszter Blahák.

therapeutic practices. There are key questions about what to collect and how to display collections in ways that are beneficial to, and respectful of, diverse perspectives – the responses to which will shape the futures of bodies in medical museums.

It is clear that with imagination, flexibility and resources, museums will find new uses and new audiences. These seemingly dead collections have life in them yet.

NOTES

1. William Hunter, *Two Introductory Lectures* (London: Johnson, 1784), p. 56; William Hunter, *An Anatomical Description of the Human Gravid Uterus and its Contents* (London: Johnson and Nicol: 1794), p. 14.

2. Rebecca Messbarger, 'The Re-Birth of Venus in Florence's Royal Museum of Physics and Natural History', *Journal of the History of Collections*, advance access published 16 May 2012, 1–21 (p. 1).

3. Carin Berkowitz, 'The Beauty of Anatomy: Visual Displays and Surgical Education in Early-Nineteenth–Century London', *Bulletin of the History of Medicine*, 85 (2011), 248–78.

4. Samuel JMM Alberti, *Morbid Curiosities: Medical Museums in Nineteenth-Century Britain* (Oxford: Oxford University Press, 2011).

5. Roslyn Poignant, *Professional Savages: Captive Lives and Western Spectacle* (New Haven: Yale University Press, 2004), pp.11–12.

6. Alan W Bates, '"Indecent and Demoralising Representations": Public Anatomy Museums in Mid-Victorian England', *Medical History*, 52 (2008), 1–22.

7. Ken Arnold and Thomas Söderqvist, 'Medical Instruments in Museums: Immediate Impressions and Historical Meanings', *Isis*, 102 (2011), 718–29.

8. Eva Åhrén and Michael Sappol, 'The Strange Space of the Body: Two Dialogues', in *Strange Spaces: Explorations Into Mediated Obscurity*, ed. by André Jansson and Amanda Lagerkvist (Burlington, VT: Ashgate, 2009), pp. 73–100.

9. *Highlights of the Collection, Medical History Museum, University of Melbourne*, ed. by Jacqueline Healy (Melbourne: University of Melbourne, 2012).

10. Elizabeth Hallam, 'Anatomical Design: Making and Using Three-Dimensional Models of the Human Body', in *Design Anthropology: Theory and Practice* ed. by Wendy Gunn, Ton Otto and Rachel Charlotte Smith (London: Berg, 2013).

11. Kathleen Jamie, *Findings* (London: Sort Of Books, 2005).

12. Karen Ingham, *Narrative Remains* (London: Royal College of Surgeons of England, 2009).

13. Neil Curtis, 'Thinking about the Right Home: Repatriation and the University of Aberdeen', in *Utimut: Past Heritage – Future Partnerships, Discussions on Repatriation in the 21st Century*, ed. by Mille Gabriel and Jens Dahl (Copenhagen, 2007), pp. 44–55.

The organic museum

The Hunterian and other collections at the Royal College of Surgeons of England

Samuel JMM Alberti

The Hunterian Museum is one of several collections at the Royal College of Surgeons in London, and in its present form only the latest manifestation of the impulse to display human remains and medical artefacts evident over the past two centuries. Since 1813 the college has exhibited a range of objects for a variety of purposes to a changing audience. Museums played crucial roles in nineteenth and twentieth-century science and medicine in general and in this institution in particular, and although their purpose has changed, collections continue to be important today. This chapter explores the role of this material culture in medical training, heritage and professional identity by discussing the collections and their visitors. What kinds of objects has the college displayed, why, and to whom?

GENESIS

At the core of the college's museums are the remains of the eighteenth-century collection of the surgeon–anatomist John Hunter (Figure 1). Having worked on preparations for his elder brother, the physician and man-midwife William Hunter (who bequeathed his own collections to the University of Glasgow), John set about amassing what would become by his death in 1793 a 14,000-specimen collection (Figure 2). Among them

FIGURE 1 (OPPOSITE)
Portrait of John Hunter by Joshua Reynolds, 1786.
Hunterian Museum at the Royal College of Surgeons.

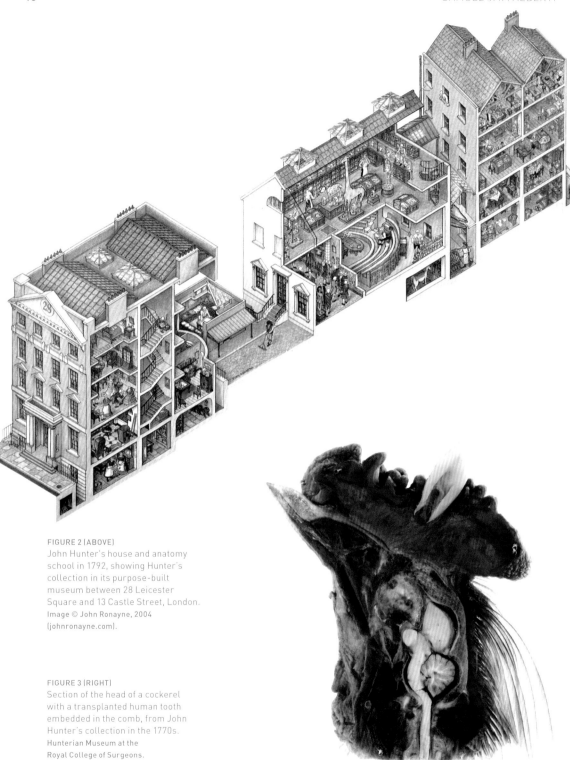

FIGURE 2 (ABOVE)
John Hunter's house and anatomy
school in 1792, showing Hunter's
collection in its purpose-built
museum between 28 Leicester
Square and 13 Castle Street, London.
Image © John Ronayne, 2004
(johnronayne.com).

FIGURE 3 (RIGHT)
Section of the head of a cockerel
with a transplanted human tooth
embedded in the comb, from John
Hunter's collection in the 1770s.
Hunterian Museum at the
Royal College of Surgeons.

were preparations showing not only healthy and morbid human anatomy but also comparative anatomy. These zoological specimens demonstrated 'the animal œconomy' (what would now be called physiology) and 'generation', that is, reproduction and development.[1] John Hunter used his collections to teach anatomy students and to demonstrate his research, including early experiments in transplantation (Figure 3). His interest in comparing human and animal would have echoes over the next two centuries, as we shall see.

The government eventually acquired Hunter's collection and, after the Royal College of Physicians declined, assigned it to the Company of Surgeons in 1799. The Company had recently acquired land on Lincoln's Inn Fields and erected a building that would do justice to this renowned collection. The museum dominated George Dance's architectural structure (Figure 4) and was a major factor in gaining the charter that established the Royal College of Surgeons in London.

The board of trustees created to oversee Hunter's collection expanded it further during the decade it took to complete the building. The trustees entreated college members to send 'such Preparations, Fragments, Specimens, Casts, Drawings, Engravings, Manuscripts and Books, as you may be able to procure, at Home or Abroad, and which may be likely in any Degree to enlarge the Sphere, or facilitate the Attainment of knowledge, respecting the Productions, Organization, Functions, Changes, or Varieties, Of animals'.[2]

Finally, on 18 May 1813, the college opened the museum. Even then, it was available only to members of the college, at noon and two o'clock on Tuesdays and Thursdays, for certain months in the year. Visitors were met by the beadle in his gown and directed to the galleries, where the specimens were explained by the conservator, William Clift (who as a youth had been Hunter's assistant and had remained with the collections ever since). Visitors were neither permitted to draw the preparations without permission nor touch them: thankfully, 'the

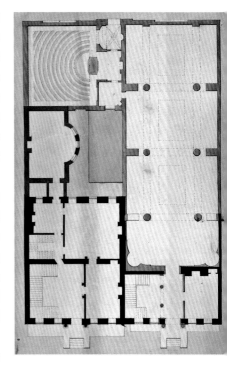

FIGURE 4
Ground floor plan of the 1813 building showing the extent of the museum.
Archives of the Royal College of Surgeons of England.

utmost order and decorum prevailed'.[3] The Prince Regent was among the early visitors, who were otherwise surgeons, fellows of the Royal College of Physicians, or invited 'students of the healing art, Professors and scientific men'.[4] After considerable debate between the college and the board concerning opening restrictions (and egged on by *The Lancet*), eventually in 1831 the museum opened for a third day each week.[5] Nevertheless, at a time when anatomy had become a key element of medical education and museums were equally important as dissecting rooms as places to teach anatomy, the collection was a model for other museums in Britain and beyond.[6]

By this time Clift was assisted by the young surgeon–naturalist Richard Owen, later Clift's son-in-law and successor. During his three decades at the college Owen established himself as the foremost comparative anatomist in the country, and styled the museum as the national collection of natural science. Access was enlarged to allow learned men and 'respectably dressed Persons' more generally to visit (Figure 5).[7] Among them was the journalist Frederick Knight Hunt, who found himself 'amidst an abundant harvest of death to teach the lesson of how life continues'; he left impressed by 'this bony parliament of natural creation'.[8]

Fridays and Saturdays, meanwhile, were set aside for researchers, as Owen positioned the museum as the pre-eminent centre for natural history. The college authorities were generally content about this, except for Owen's emphasis on his own specialist field, palaeontology, the utility of which was not so evident for the training of surgeons. Eventually in 1856 – in high dudgeon – Owen left to take over the natural history collections at the British Museum (eventually he would remove them to South Kensington to establish what is now the Natural History Museum).

ZENITH

In Owen's wake his successors were careful to maintain the medical utility of the collections, while nonetheless concentrating

FIGURE 5
Richard Owen shows visitors prehistoric specimens in the larger of the two galleries that comprised the museum in 1842. Watercolour by Thomas Hosmer Shepherd. Hunterian Museum at the Royal College of Surgeons.

FIGURE 6
Room 1 of 5 of the college
museum, around 1900.
Hunterian Museum at the
Royal College of Surgeons.

on their own specialist areas: John Thomas Quekett's microscopy and William Henry Flower's skeletal zoology. In addition, in the latter nineteenth century there was a renewed emphasis on the pathological parts of the collection, especially under the watchful eye of the prominent surgeon–pathologist James Paget. By the turn of the century researchers, medical practitioners and students could view some of the 45,000 specimens (Figure 6) from 10 o'clock every weekday. From 1882, women were granted admission – but only on certain days.

Over the nineteenth century the Royal College of Surgeons was as much a site for biological research as it was for medical study. In the early twentieth century, however, physical anthropology dominated, thanks to Arthur Keith, conservator from 1908 (Figure 7). Human evolutionary development and ethnic diversity featured in new acquisitions and displays (Figure 8). Keith also oversaw the arrival of some 5,000 skulls and teeth collected by the Odontological Society of Great Britain. (Odontology is the scientific study of teeth.)

Another shift in the function of medical collections was evident at Lincoln's Inn Fields and in other museums by the turn of the century. From the 1870s, members began to donate interesting surgical instruments to the college museum, which thus became a site for heritage as well as training, for commemorating as well as learning surgery. This was certainly the case by 1912, when the college acquired antisepsis pioneer Joseph Lister's instrument cabinet, enshrining with objects the elevated status of surgery shortly after Lister had become the first medical practitioner to join the House of Lords.

This emphasis on the history of surgery has remained evident ever since but at the outbreak of the World War I, present-day clinical benefit for the living was foremost in the curators' minds. Keith and his staff wanted to contribute to the war effort and, in concert with the Royal Army Medical Corps, he established a clinical 'war museum' to aid the training of military medical personnel (Figures 9 and 10), which included specimens demonstrating the effects of gas attacks and bullet wounds.

The war museum remained an important part of the displays in the inter-war period, when like collections across Europe and North America – not least the natural history museums in London and New York – the college museum was at the apex of its size and status. A range of educational groups and other visitors (more than 10,000 per year) came to study some 65,000 objects. One British surgeon remembered: 'It was the standard collection for anatomists in our Empire and from most parts of the world.'[9] Nevertheless, some of the legacies of previous uses and emphases were becoming redundant. Noting that the zoological material was no longer as useful, the college began to transfer this part of the collection to the British Museum (Natural History). Whale skeletons were removed because they 'overshadowed' the pathology collection in both senses (Figure 11). Rather than natural history, 'the human body', explained Keith, 'its structure, growth, its physiology and its pathology—must be the text of the discourse preached by the

contents of the Museum'. Its purpose was 'to serve as a great reference library, which may meet the needs of medical men, of biologists, and of medical students. Above all, it has to meet the needs of those engaged in medical and surgical research.' This 'immense consulting library', was now to be split between those specimens on display for education and those behind the scenes for research.[10]

PHOENIX

Keith's 'engine of research' met an untimely end in May 1941 when around two-thirds of the collection was destroyed during an air raid (Figure 12).[11] After the war, the college assessed the continued educational demand for museums and formed four distinct collections: the remains of the Hunterian Museum; the Odontological Museum, which had largely survived the bombing; and two new teaching collections in the anatomy and pathological departments respectively. Thanks to funding from the Wellcome Foundation in 1945, collections were embedded into the laboratory facilities established in the 1950s within the

FIGURE 9 (LEFT)
Ink and pencil drawing of Private Walter Ashworth by Henry Tonks, part of a series showing patients treated by plastic surgeon Harold Gillies and colleagues at Queen Mary's Hospital, Sidcup, during and after World War I.
Hunterian Museum at the
Royal College of Surgeons.

FIGURE 10 (RIGHT)
Private Ashworth during the latter part of his treatment, pastel by Henry Tonks, 1917.
Hunterian Museum at the
Royal College of Surgeons.

Workmen and museum staff moving
the bones of the Greenland whale
out of the college for transit to the
Natural History Museum, June 1934.
Hunterian Museum at the
Royal College of Surgeons.

remits of the professors of anatomy and of pathology on the third and fourth floors of the building that was erected to house the new Institute of Basic Medical Sciences.

Throughout these post-war collections, specimens were displayed alongside x-rays, clinical illustrations and textbooks. They were used intensely by medical researchers and students and by the 500 postgraduates at the institute. The museums also welcomed several thousand other visitors each year, predominantly nurses, dentists and school groups. Special exhibitions were staged for medical and scientific congresses.

The controversial anatomist and anthropologist Frederic Wood Jones became professor of anatomy at the college in 1945. He set about reformulating the surviving collections along Hunter's original lines, appointing his former assistant Jessie Dobson, who had helped recover the collection after the bombing,

as 'recorder of the collection' (Figure 13). Dobson painstakingly worked through the specimens and reconnected them to their Hunterian origins and arrangement, establishing herself as a historical authority in the process, and cementing the museum's heritage function by elevating the founding collection to the status of 'a precious relic and a memorial to [Hunter's] work'.[12]

FIGURE 12
View of the south east corner of Museum Room 2, with doorway into Room 3, showing a man standing amid the debris after the bombing in May 1941.
Associated Newspapers/Solo Syndication.

MEMORIAL

It was this Hunterian Museum that opened in a new custom-built space on the first floor in May 1963 (the 150th anniversary of the first museum opening), with the Odontological Museum next door. Despite the college council's intention to open it to anyone over 17 years of age, the board of trustees was reluctant. Rather, the Hunterian Museum was available to 'Diplomates of the college and other duly qualified medical men and women:

[...] to Medical Students: to members of learned and scientific bodies' or to those obtaining written permission. A twentieth-century museum thereby maintained Victorian admission protocols. Although it kept some of its research and medical training function, it was the museums upstairs, open only to the medically trained and those in training, which were more active in this regard (all of them open all day, five days per week – the Hunterian Museum also on Saturday mornings). The Wellcome Museum of Pathology's curator, the senior lecturer in pathology MS Israel, insisted it was not 'a static mausoleum' but rather 'a dynamic revelation of pathological processes' and, like its anatomical equivalent, it was still in use for college examinations.[13]

The Hunterian collection was now used mostly as a tool for heritage, evidenced in particular at the celebrations of Hunter's 250th birthday in 1978: it was what Arnold and Chaplin (in this volume) dub a 'post-medical' museum. The Hunterian collection was complemented in this respect by distinct collections of historical instruments (Figure 14), anaesthetic equipment, ceramics, medals and artworks (each with their own honorary curator). Thanks to Arthur Keith, the college also owned and ran Charles Darwin's former residence, Down House, as a museum.

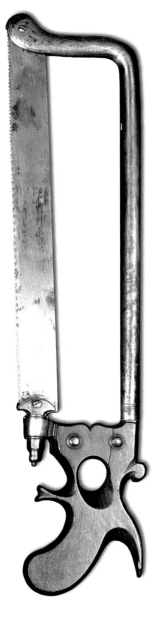

Dobson's successor Elizabeth Allen maintained in 1986 that the collections still comprised 'a teaching resource for undergraduate and postgraduate medical students, student nurses, veterinary students and senior school pupils', while 'assistance [was] given to medical historians and historical background for publications and lectures'.[14] It was clear by the 1990s, however, that the status of museums within medical education and the surgical profession had changed, and these dispersed collections were difficult to manage. They were therefore supervised by a new 'Keeper of College Collections', Stella Mason, and a more general audience was invited to the Hunterian Museum. Against the apparently incongruous responses to retained organs scandals in 1999 on the one hand and the popularity of Gunther von Hagens' *Body Worlds* exhibitions on the other, the college, board and a new staff of museum professionals secured £3.2 million for a refurbishment completed in 2005 (Figure 15).

ATTRACTION

Together with a re-invigorated Odontological Museum and a dedicated collection for trainees and professionals (the Wellcome Museum of Anatomy and Pathology, combining the two post-war collections), the Royal College of Surgeons museums are now used more than they have ever been. At the time of writing, some 75,000 visits are made each year to the Hunterian Museum, attracted by the refurbished displays and a vibrant exhibition and events programme. The collections are thereby linked to developments in surgery, current events (for example, sports surgery in 2012 to coincide with the Olympics and Paralympics, see Figure 16) and commemorative activities (such as the centenary of the outbreak of World War I). Displaying not only human and animal remains but also historical surgical instruments, its heritage function is an important part of the professional identity of the college's members.

In the Wellcome Museum of Anatomy and Pathology 7,000 students and junior doctors avail themselves of training opportunities each year, as surgical tutors juxtapose specimens with three-dimensional simulations and training films. The Museums and Archives Department (formed in 2010) helps more than 1,000 researchers on historical, medical and scientific projects each year, including a number of biological studies, echoing Hunter's, Owen's and Flower's passions.

As ways to engage the public with science and medicine and their histories, as material manifestations of surgeons' professional identity, as training tools and research resources, medical museums at the Royal College of Surgeons and elsewhere are incomparable. They will remain important resources for research and teaching as long as those with the privilege of their custody continue to adapt them to new techniques, uses and audiences.

NOTES

1. Simon Chaplin, 'John Hunter and The "Museum Oeconomy", 1750–1800' (PhD thesis, King's College London, 2009).
2. Royal College of Surgeons Archives (RCS), Museum Committee Minute Book 16 June 1804.
3. RCS Board of Curators 2 July 1813.
4. RCS Museum Committee Minute Book 3 June 1824.
5. See for example, 'Meeting of the Trustees of the Hunterian Museum', *The Lancet*, 10 (1826), 339–41.
6. Samuel JMM Alberti, *Morbid Curiosities: Medical Museums in Nineteenth-Century Britain* (Oxford: Oxford University Press, 2011).
7. RCS Board of Curators 9 October 1841.
8. Frederick Knight Hunt, 'The Hunterian Museum', *Household Words*, 33 (1850), p. 278.
9. George Grey Turner, *The Hunterian Museum: Yesterday and To-morrow* (London: Cassell, 1946), p. 52.
10. RCS Annual Report on the Museum 1925, p. 3; 1928, p. 2 and 1925, p. 2.
11. RCS Annual Report on the Museum 1941, p. 2.
12. Turner, *The Hunterian Museum*, p. 65.
13. RCS Memorandum on Wellcome Museum of Pathology 7 June 1972.
14. RCS Hunterian Institute Annual Report 1986, p. 13.

FIGURE 15 (OPPOSITE)
The 'Crystal Gallery' in the 2005 refurbishment of the Hunterian Museum.
Hunterian Museum at the Royal College of Surgeons.

FIGURE 16 (BELOW)
Sprinting by Richard Neave and Denise Smith (2012), a wax écorché of runner Richard Whitehead commissioned for the *Anatomy of an Athlete* exhibition.
Hunterian Museum at the Royal College of Surgeons.

Museums within a museum

Surgeons' Hall, the Royal College of Surgeons of Edinburgh

Chris Henry

Visitors to the Pathology Museum of the Royal College of Surgeons of Edinburgh are often affected by the grand setting in which the objects are displayed (Figure 1). The cathedral-like quality of the exhibition space and the many ranks of preserved specimens, collected over centuries, still perhaps reflect the interests and values of an earlier age. Yet, although contemporary museum visitors tend to expect multimedia displays, people flock to see this part of the building in its late-Georgian grandeur: there are about 30,000 visitors to the museum each year, mainly members of the general public. This impressive structure was built to act as a powerful physical representation of the college, but the building was always intended to be a centre of learning and a museum. It is here that nineteenth-century medical students could see diseased organs in ways that were not possible on hospital wards.[1]

Today, the Pathology Museum – the upper part of the Playfair Hall – connects with the Jules Thorn History of Surgery Museum, which was installed in 1989. The Dental Museum contains the collection of Dr John Menzies Campbell, and is one of the largest dental collections in the world (Figures 2, 3 and 4). These three collections are known collectively as Surgeons' Hall Museum, containing 23,000 objects, including at least

FIGURE 1 (OPPOSITE)
View of the ground floor of the Pathology Museum, 2012, with display cases made in 1829.
Courtesy of the Royal College of Surgeons of Edinburgh.

15,000 specimens ranging from fully articulated skeletons to the tiny bones of the inner ear. The college's museum is thus an aggregate of collections that have been assembled over time. But whereas in many other institutions the display areas are usually called 'galleries', in the college they are all still referred to as separate museums. These museums have been shaped by the interests of curators and conservators employed at the college. Current displays make use of texts and images, and recent developments have included some computerised audiovisual displays, but these are intended to complement the nineteenth-century setting. For the built interior of the Pathology Museum has been kept much as it was when architect William Playfair saw its construction during the early 1830s, yet since then there have also been some notable changes in the displays, as this chapter outlines.

BUILDING COLLECTIONS

The college has existed in various forms since 1505, with its Seal of Cause ratified by James IV in 1506. By the end of the seventeenth century, as the Incorporation of Barber Surgeons, it was 'making a collection of all natural and artificial curiosities', and advertising in the *Edinburgh Gazette* for donations of books

FIGURE 2 (LEFT)
Dentist George Fellows Harrington's clockwork dental drill, 1865.
Courtesy of the Royal College of Surgeons of Edinburgh.

FIGURE 3 (RIGHT)
18th-century French illustration of tooth extraction, held in the Menzies Campbell Collection. The caption states: 'It's nothing' – presumably not from the patient's painful point of view.
Courtesy of the Royal College of Surgeons of Edinburgh.

and artefacts (Figure 5).[2] The book and specimen collection was transferred to the University of Edinburgh in the eighteenth century, when the Incorporation was undergoing financial problems, and the book collection is still kept at the University Library. Despite this move, the college retained significant items, such as the preserved body of an executed prisoner dissected in 1702, whose dissection was the first recorded at Surgeons' Hall and was overseen by Archibald Pitcairne (Figure 6).[3] Having divested itself of the barbers in 1722, the college, along with the University Medical School, rapidly became part of Scotland's medical learning infrastructure in the eighteenth century (Figure 7).

During the 1820s there was considerable expansion of the collections. The specimens of the eminent anatomist John Barclay were given to the college, with the requirement that a building

FIGURE 4
Display showing 19th and 20th-
century equipment for manufacturing
dentures in the Dental Museum, 2012.
Courtesy of the Royal College
of Surgeons of Edinburgh.

FIGURE 5
A Surgical Demonstration, Rotterdam,
around 1700. The demonstration was
performed upon a corpse. A Van der Groes.
Courtesy of the Royal College of
Surgeons of Edinburgh.

FIGURE 6
The anatomised body of David
Mylles, an executed criminal
dissected in 1702 at Surgeons' Hall.
Courtesy of the Royal College
of Surgeons of Edinburgh.

be prepared for them – the main reason for the construction of Playfair Hall. In addition, the collection of anatomist and surgeon Charles Bell was purchased for a hefty £3,000 in 1825 (Figure 8). Bell's collection was particularly significant, having developed at Bell's Great Windmill Street School of Anatomy in London, which was established by William Hunter.

For the Royal College of Surgeons of Edinburgh, 1832 was a monumental year. The Playfair building opened as the college's new home, with the museum as a primary learning resource. In the same year, the Anatomy Act was passed in the wake of the Burke and Hare affair. This scandal had broken following the murder of sixteen people by William Burke and William Hare, Irish labourers who supplied corpses for dissection at the anatomy school of renowned surgeon and lecturer Robert Knox.[4] Knox had been appointed the first conservator of the collections from 1926, having had strong working connections with Barclay, and he was a driving force behind the creation of the Playfair building.

The college distanced itself from Knox following the scandal and he eventually left for London in 1842. He was followed as conservator by William MacGillivray in 1831. MacGillivray studied natural history and he threw himself into the role of conservator for the next ten years. He transferred material to the new building and a new printed catalogue was released in 1835.[5]

MacGillivray resigned in 1841 to become professor of natural history at Marischal College in Aberdeen (see Hallam in this volume). A spirit of parsimony descended over the museum. The President questioned the cost of the museum and the conservator's salary. John Goodsir became the next conservator and, although he had a good grasp of the problems associated with the collections, it seems that little was done to expand or interpret them until the arrival of Charles Walker Cathcart.[6]

Appointed as conservator in 1887, Cathcart donated many specimens and initiated a new catalogue, which became

FIGURE 7 (ABOVE)
Watercolour of Old Surgeons'
Hall. The portraits of Edinburgh
medical men were by or after
John Kay, around 1796.
Courtesy of the Royal College
of Surgeons of Edinburgh.

FIGURE 9
Corrosion cast of blood
vesselsin a human foot,
probably 19th century.
Courtesy of the Royal College
of Surgeons of Edinburgh.

FIGURE 8
Bust of Charles Bell by
William Theed, 1851.
Courtesy of the Royal College
of Surgeons of Edinburgh.

an enduring symbol of his work at the college (Figure 9).[7] It provided a framework and index that defined types of disease and their locations in the body. With the expansion of laboratory facilities for the museum came many histology specimens and photomicrographs (photographs taken through a microscope), and histology still forms a major part of the collections (approximately 15,000 items). Cathcart worked for thirteen years as conservator, followed by Theodore Shennan, David Waterston, and then Henry Wade.

TWENTIETH-CENTURY DEVELOPMENTS

From an architectural perspective, the college underwent extensive changes around 1909, when architect Arthur Balfour Paul – who had previously designed the interiors of ocean

FIGURE 10
Photomontage of portraits set in the Main Hall of the Royal College of Surgeons, 1902. It shows the hall prior to changes made by architect Arthur Balfour Paul. Photograph by Barclay Bros. Courtesy of the Royal College of Surgeons of Edinburgh.

liners – extended the building and redesigned some of the interior, introducing many of the features that can be seen today (Figure 10). In particular, the area where the Jules Thorn History of Surgery Museum is now located was altered, and the Barclayan Hall Museum was converted into the Main Hall, where all college meetings and ceremonial activities take place.

The two world wars significantly affected the college and its museum – and many other museums as well. During World War I, Wade left to serve in Palestine, and the post was taken up by Frank Jardine as interim conservator from 1914 to 1919. By the time David Middleton Greig became conservator in 1921, he was an internationally known pathologist. Greig added to the existing collections with, for instance, some 300 human skulls. By this time the museum contained a wide range of specimens, instruments, histological specimens, photographs and relevant publications (Figure 11). This led to a trend in which the post of conservator was given to a senior fellow of the college, who was expected to run and develop the museum. Individual conservators continued to favour particular types of specimen and this tended to strengthen the collections in selected areas. For example, a wide range of specimens has been acquired in relation to orthopaedics (the treatment of bones and muscles).

While collections expanded after World War I, during World War II they were hidden in the basement for fear of destruction by aerial attack (see Alberti in this volume). After 1945, James Norman Jackson Hartley's primary motivation as conservator was to present specimens for postgraduate research. During the 1950s many items were disposed of but others were acquired and the dentistry and radiology collections were enhanced. During the 1960s displays included a series of foetal specimens showing skeletal development, texts and images on the stomach, intestine, rectum and gall bladder, and nineteenth-century plaster casts of African people (Figure 12).

DEC Mekie was a prominent figure who shaped perceptions of the museum (Figure 13). Indeed, he wrote a history of it in

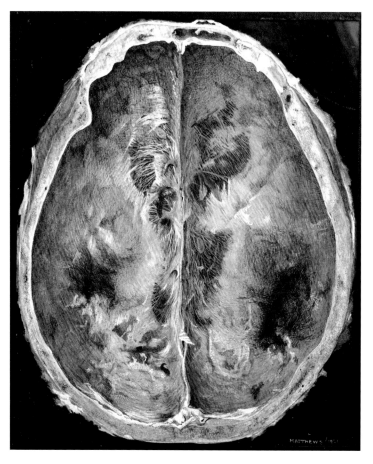

1982, with Violet Tansey, a long-time employee at the museum.[8]
Having been appointed professor of clinical surgery at King
Edward VII College of Medicine in Singapore in 1936, and
interned there during World War II, he became conservator of
the college museum in 1955. He reorganised the huge collection
of pathological, anatomical and historical material and improved
the displays. From this work emerged his publication, *A Colour
Atlas of Demonstrations in Surgical Pathology* (1983–86).

CHANGES AND CHALLENGES

In its present arrangement, as already noted, Surgeons' Hall
Museum consists of several collections, each of which concerns

a particular subject or specialty. This is most evident in the Pathology Museum. The ground floor is arranged according to themes and addresses a wide range of subjects including military surgery, parasites, maxillofacial surgery and childbirth. Exhibition space is dedicated to key figures in the history of the college, such as the surgeon Joseph Bell, and the medically trained Arthur Conan Doyle, author of the Sherlock Holmes detective stories. This approach builds on the changing interests and values of the many conservators who have told the story of the objects in their care. Above the ground-floor exhibitions, there are displays of specimens used for medical teaching in the upper gallery; an area that is specifically intended for

medical professionals and is currently closed to the public
except for specially arranged guided tours and educational
groups (Figure 14).

    Since the introduction of the Human Tissue (Scotland)
Act in 2006, greater consideration has been given to legal and
ethical concerns with regard to the display of human remains.
This difficult subject poses challenges for the exhibition team,
especially as there are many conflicting opinions and perspectives
involved in the viewing and interpretation of human remains. The
museum strives to address issues of health and disease with
ever-greater participation from visitors. A recent exhibition, *Skin
Deep* (2010), emphasises the relationship between psychology
and surgery, and aims to foster greater understanding of those

FIGURE 14
View, in 2012, of Playfair Museum's
upper gallery displaying early 19th-
century pathological specimens.
Courtesy of the Royal College
of Surgeons of Edinburgh.

with facial deformities. Although the displays continue to focus on scientific approaches to the body and surgery, artists and poets have been encouraged to engage with the collections to provide different insights into these subjects. It is hoped that such insights deepen understanding of physical affliction and disability (Figure 15).

The museum's role has been continually adapted since it was created, so that it is no longer simply a specialist collection for medical students. With this widening of audience, however, its medical relevance still continues. Occasionally, surgical

FIGURE 15
Prosthetic arm for a
baby, around 1998.
Courtesy of the Royal College
of Surgeons of Edinburgh.

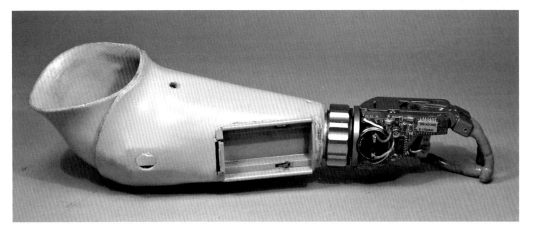

examiners use specimens from the collection to highlight particular conditions. The specimens act as valuable records of diseases and new forms of research using the collections are appearing regularly. There have been a number of requests to take DNA samples. The latest research projects carried out by the Department of Forensic Anthropology at the University of Dundee have used several specimens as the basis for students' research. For example, Lydia Carline researched a syphilitic skull in 2011 to examine this condition and then to reconstruct the facial appearance. Research is an important aspect of work at Surgeons' Hall Museum, as it strives to enhance understanding of its collections as well as offering insights into the latest surgical techniques (Figure 16).

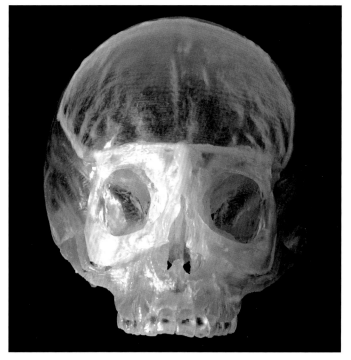

In the past fifteen years, the single most important change in the use of the museum has been in the shift from limited access to publically accessible space. This is not entirely new as records for 1839, for instance, indicate that 10,256 members of the general public visited the museum in that year.[9] In the twenty-first century the college council supports the museum's development, recognising it as a valuable asset for promoting public understanding of what surgeons do, and what their motivations are. Since 2009 the college has begun a campaign to upgrade the museum and new technology is being introduced. A new initiative, 'The Lister Project', has been devised. This heritage programme aims to increase visitor participation and physical access to the exhibits, as well as widening the remit of displays to include issues of gender and patients' experiences. The UK's Heritage Lottery Fund is assisting this transformation, which will include public access to the displays of 3,000 specimens previously closed to the public in the upper gallery of the Pathology Museum. New developments will also feature an all-glass lift at the entrance to the college serving all floors and galleries, an audiovisual theatre based on an eighteenth-century anatomy theatre, temporary exhibition space, and an education workshop area. These facilities will open out the museum so that many more visitors from all sorts of backgrounds can learn not only about medical history but also about their own bodies.

NOTES

1. Steve Sturdy, 'Making Sense in the Pathology Museum', in *Anatomy Acts: How We Come To Know Ourselves*, ed. by Andrew Patrizio and Dawn Kemp (Edinburgh: Birlinn, 2006), pp. 109–117.

2. Quoted in Violet Tansey and David Eric Cameron Mekie, *The Museum of the Royal College of Surgeons of Edinburgh* (Edinburgh: Royal College of Surgeons of Edinburgh, 1982), p. 1.

3. Helen M Dingwall, *'A Famous and Flourishing Society': The History of the Royal College of Surgeons of Edinburgh, 1505–2005* (Edinburgh: Edinburgh University Press, 2005).

4. Ruth Richardson, *Death, Dissection and the Destitute*, 2nd edn (London: Phoenix Press, 2001).

5. Clarendon Hyde Creswell, The Royal College of Surgeons of Edinburgh. Historical Notes from 1505 to 1905 (Edinburgh: Royal College of Surgeons of Edinburgh, 1926). Catalogue of the Museum of the Royal College of Surgeons of Edinburgh (Edinburgh: Neill, 1836).

6. Tansey and Mekie, *The Museum of the Royal College*, p. 23.

7. Charles Walker Cathcart, *Descriptive Catalogue of the Anatomical and Pathological Specimens in the Museum of the Royal College of Surgeons of Edinburgh* (Edinburgh: Thin, 1893).

8. Tansey and Mekie, *The Museum of the Royal College*.

9. Creswell, *The Royal College of Surgeons*, p. 85.

Disappearing museums?

Medical collections at the University of Aberdeen

Elizabeth Hallam

Innumerable medical museums have emerged and thrived in Europe and the United States over the past two centuries only to subsequently disappear. Deliberate destruction, calculated dismantling, dispersal and re-arrangement, consignment to storage, and unplanned disintegration, especially since the mid-twentieth century, have all played their part in the disappearance of these often massive collections along with the buildings and rooms that have housed them. There are many factors involved in these processes, from the unstable material composition of organic museum objects to the motives of the people who create and care for these items. Museums appear and disappear within wider social and cultural settings that guide what is seen, hidden or disposed of.

The making and breaking of medical museums at the University of Aberdeen in north-east Scotland is explored in this chapter. The first decade of the 1900s saw many museums flourishing at the university's Marischal College but few had survived a century later. The anatomy museum, used mainly to teach students of medicine, was one of these. What contributed to its survival, and why did so many of the college's other medical museums whither or perish? This story begins at Marischal

College with lavish ceremonial and concludes with evacuation and demolition but not an end.

OPENING

September 1906: King Edward VII and Queen Alexandra opened the newly extended college buildings and participated in a celebration of the university's 400th anniversary (Figure 1).[1] The festivities included four days of extravagant balls and musical performances, sports, processions, banqueting and fireworks, enjoyed by thousands of guests, city and university elites and eminent visitors from around the globe. At the final evening's reception the public was invited to tour the college's museums to view what were perhaps the most impressive displays of

FIGURE 1
View of the royal procession arriving at the entrance to Marischal College, 27 September 1906, by photographers George Washington Wilson and Co. University of Aberdeen.

collected items in the university's four-hundred-year history. The route that visitors took through electrically lit chambers, corridors and staircases, in what was billed as the world's largest granite building, promoted the college as a major centre for medicine and science.[2]

From cellar to attic, photographic dark rooms, workshops, laboratories, libraries, stores and teaching rooms all facilitated research and teaching. This powerhouse for producing and communicating knowledge required an abundance of specimens, living and dead, so the relevant departments in the college had 'animal houses', aquaria and preparation rooms for dissecting and preserving. In addition to museums of chemistry, geology, botany, agriculture, education, natural history and anthropology – the latter comprising numerous 'objects illustrating the habits and customs of different races of mankind' – there were major collections for the study of human bodies in health and disease.[3] The natural history museum (from around the mid 1800s) and the anthropological museum (when removed from the anatomy department's anthropometric laboratory in 1907) were intended for university uses *and* public viewing – both museums occupying prominent galleries in Marischal College's front quadrangle.[4] However, the medical collections in 1906 (and

since) were intended primarily for use by university teachers and their students, with access restricted mainly to this audience.

The pathology museum exhibited hundreds of specimens in glass jars showing diseases, and painted plaster casts of 'morbid organs' made under the direction of David Hamilton, professor of pathology. The surgery museum held around 1,600 specimens acquired by professor of surgery, Alexander Ogston – who had studied with Rudolf Virchow in Berlin (see Schnalke in this volume) – and by his predecessor William Pirrie (in post 1860 to 1882).[5] There were rows of surgical instruments and boxes of microscope slides, x-ray images revealed bone fractures, and an ophthalmic collection focused on the human eye.[6] The midwifery museum's specimens pertained to pregnancy, including pathological exhibits of diseased organs. Here too were specialist instruments, for example, forceps used in birthing. In the materia medica museum substances with medicinal applications from around the world – for example, leaves, seeds, fruits and barks – were displayed. At the department of forensic medicine and public health the museum featured specimens relating to hygiene and to medical jurisprudence. The latter demonstrated conditions of medico-legal interest – for example, the effects of poisons or weapons upon the body. Francis Ogston,

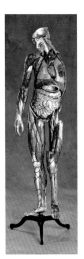

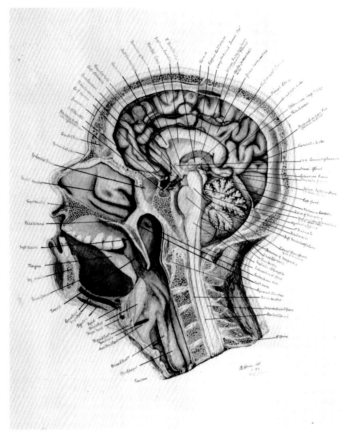

FIGURE 4 (LEFT)
Illustration of the head, by Alexander
Don, produced under the supervision
of anatomist Robert Reid, 1892. It
was part of a series of watercolours
made by Don and Arthur Hugh
Lister, nephew of surgeon Joseph
Lister, when they were medical
students at Marischal College.
University of Aberdeen.
Photograph by John McIntosh.

FIGURE 5 (OPPOSITE, TOP)
X-ray image of a museum specimen
described as 'Skiagram of
distorted foot of Chinese female',
around 1905. The x-ray image
was photographed for publication
in the *University of Aberdeen
Proceedings of The Anatomical and
Anthropological Society 1904–06*.
University of Aberdeen.

FIGURE 6 (OPPOSITE, BOTTOM)
Robert Reid (far left) and Arthur
Keith (far right) in the dissecting
room of Marischal College's anatomy
department, conducting an exam
with a medical student (centre),
around 1900. Keith was a medical
student at the college in the 1880s,
acted as external examiner in
anatomy (1898 to 1901), and later
became conservator at the Royal
College of Surgeons of England.
University of Aberdeen.

father of Alexander, assembled many of these specimens when he was professor of medical jurisprudence (1860 to 1883).[7]

Professors at Marischal College were curators of the museums associated with their subjects and were largely credited for having built up the collections. Yet these scientists were dependent on their geographically wide-ranging social networks for access to specimens, in north-east Scotland and throughout the British Empire. Many such specimens were given by local medical practitioners and by graduates working overseas, often in colonial posts. In the case of human remains, those who died in Aberdeen's poorhouses, hospitals and other institutions, and whose bodies were unclaimed by relatives, were dissected in the anatomy department prior to burial and selected

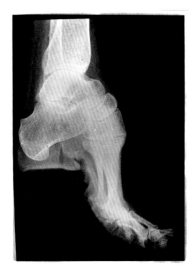

parts were preserved for its museum. Alongside specimens, the college's museums featured interrelated diagrams, drawings, photographs and models: all possible media were mobilised to train students.[8]

The anatomy museum was no exception. By 1906 its expanding collections rendered anatomy visible and tangible in two and three dimensions. From the 1860s onwards, during anatomist John Struthers' professorship (1863 to 1889), anatomical specimens – human and animal (mainly vertebrates) for the study of comparative anatomy – were gathered voraciously from land and sea (Figure 2). For inspiration in creating this museum, Struthers had looked to established and well-regarded museums at the royal colleges in London and

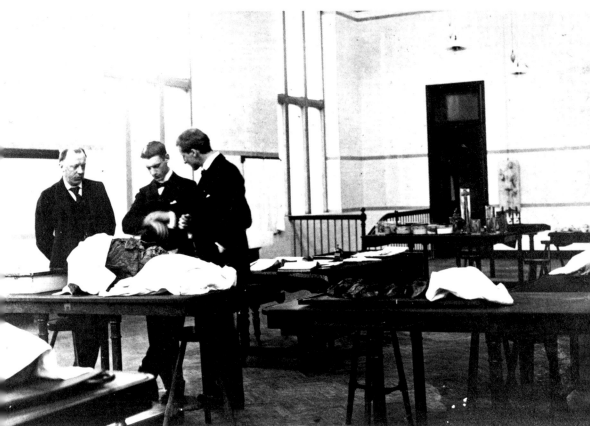

FIGURE 7 (ABOVE)
Cartoon of the 'Path. Museum', a
detail on an illustrated notice for
the medical students' class dinner
of June 1954 at the University of
Aberdeen, by 'K.J.McK'. The student
contemplates specimens of gumma
(caused by syphilis), cirrhosis of
the liver and lung cancer: diseases
associated with sex, excessive
alcohol and smoking – in which,
by implication, the student has
perhaps been indulging. Printed in
the *University of Aberdeen Album of
the Class of Medicine, 1948–1954*.
University of Aberdeen.

FIGURE 8 (OPPOSITE, TOP)
Exploded skull, purchased in
1920 from N Rouppert (previously
Tramond), a leading commercial
supplier of osteological specimens
and models in Paris – for the anatomy
museum at Marischal College.
University of Aberdeen.
Photograph by John McIntosh.

FIGURE 9 (OPPOSITE, BOTTOM)
Marischal College's anatomy
museum, 1939 to 1964.
University of Aberdeen.

Edinburgh (see Alberti, and Henry, in this volume). Anatomical models in wax, plaster and papier mâché were purchased from leading firms in France and Germany, such as Auzoux and Ziegler, further strengthening the museum as a respected place of learning (Figure 3).

Struthers' successor, Robert Reid, added specimens prepared using up-to-date techniques and materials. From the 1890s, he preserved sections of male and female bodies, cut vertically and horizontally then encased in glass. These were displayed with labelled images that aided identification of anatomical parts (Figure 4). Specimens were also x-rayed and photographed for viewing as lantern slides projected in the lecture theatre or in specialist publications (Figure 5). This visual projection increased specimens' educational capacity, as did their use in the dissecting room where students observed them in relation to the deceased bodies they anatomised (cut and analysed) (Figure 6). For students to learn 'facts', however, Reid emphasised the importance of 'actual' specimens, which he considered irreplaceable by images. In the museum, for instance, skeletons were posed to educate on human evolution, and skulls were displayed to indicate physical 'variations in the different races'. Skeletal 'prehistoric remains' of people were compared with those from 'modern' times, and the development of embryos could be seen in the form of enlarged models placed in sequences.[9]

RELOCATING

Only three decades after the 1906 celebrations the majority of Marischal College's medical museums were relocated, and in this process they were substantially reconfigured. The strategic movement of specimens between rooms for teaching purposes had been routine, and larger-scale manoeuvres came with World War I, when precious specimens were shifted to basements for safe-keeping. Specimens were also periodically disposed of: in the surgery museum, for example, those considered 'worn out' were 'destroyed'.[10] But entirely relocating collections, comprising thousands of fragile objects, from the museums of pathology, surgery, midwifery, materia medica and medical jurisprudence/hygiene was a colossal undertaking.

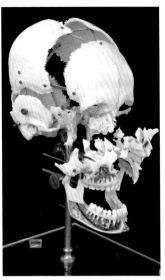

Removed from the college's neo-gothic architecture around 1938, these collections were amalgamated to create a single museum in the 'modern style' medical school at Foresterhill, a site out of the town centre where Aberdeen's hospitals were newly built. This streamlined museum was further incorporated into clinical teaching, and its displays of pathology and surgery became prominent.[11] In the 1950s the 'Path Museum' was a familiar sight among students, as evidenced in their satirical cartoons (Figure 7). Currently, around 2,000 items survive from this museum, but the 4,600ft²

space they once occupied was re-purposed in the 1990s, and the collection is now in storage. The collection is, however, utilised for temporary displays, in cases near the medical library (also at Foresterhill), on subjects such as cervical cancer and tuberculosis.[12]

Back at Marischal College, just prior to the 1939 outbreak of war, decisions regarding the anatomy department were to influence its museum for decades to come. Robert Lockhart, in his first year as professor of anatomy, supplied plans for a new department at Foresterhill but his negotiations with senior university officials reached deadlock. Having trained at Marischal College, like his predecessors Reid and Alexander Low, Lockhart knew its facilities well, and he had gained experience in planning a new medical school while professor of anatomy at the University of Birmingham. Now back at his alma mater, Lockhart made substantial demands for rooms and equipment at what would be his dream department, emphasising the importance of the museum. But when these could not be met the only solution was for the department to remain in place.[13] This failed plan – too ambitious and expensive to realise

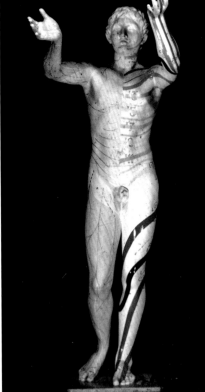

– contributed, albeit unintentionally, to the anatomy museum's longevity. By remaining at Marischal College, which was emptied of its other expanding university departments over the twentieth century, the museum escaped detrimental encroachment upon its space.

TRANSFORMING

In post-war Britain, debates about the future of medical museums highlighted a range of possibilities, from destruction to investment; after 1945 these museums were on mixed trajectories. There was extensive museum reconstruction after bomb damage at the Royal College of Surgeons of England (see Alberti in this volume), but other medical museums fared less well: one at St Thomas' Hospital in London was dismantled, and the University of Birmingham's medical school collections diminished.[14] At Marischal College key shifts in collecting and display ensured a healthy anatomy museum. While the influx of human and animal remains acquired through contacts overseas dwindled – especially with the British Empire in decline as colonised territories gained independence[15] – developments

FIGURE 12 (ABOVE)
Plaster cast of a classical figure, by Domenico Brucciani's London-based firm, purchased for Marischal College's anatomy department around 1881. The white plaster cast was painted in colour during the 1950s to form a model of dermatomes (areas of skin supplied by the same spinal nerves). The model was linked to corresponding illustrations in Robert D Lockhart, Gordon F Hamilton and Forest W Fyfe, *Anatomy of the Human Body* (London: Faber and Faber, 1959). University of Aberdeen.

in anatomical practices opened up new avenues for collecting. Keenly interested in 'living anatomy', Lockhart ensured that specimens and models obtained in the past were carefully preserved (Figure 8), while also rejuvenating the museum's displays. Skeletons were arranged to emphasise movement as though alive. The skeleton of a horse, for example, was articulated into a rearing motion and accompanied by a dismounted human rider (Figure 9). Display techniques thus aimed to animate.

Training students to view museum specimens in terms of living anatomy, Lockhart collected visual images showing bodily movement, which he displayed as slides projected in lectures. Cuttings from magazines and newspapers and photographs of artists' paintings were assembled, especially images of popular performers such as acrobats and circus entertainers. He produced anatomical films on the action of muscles and photographs of medical students posed as living models; students then observed these images of bodies alive in relation to dissecting-room bodies and museum specimens (Figure 10).[16] These strategies brought the anatomy museum to life. Lockhart's collaborations with colleagues and artists, including Alberto Morrocco, produced hundreds of illustrations for a new textbook, *Anatomy of the Human Body* (1959), and the originals were displayed like pages of a giant book in a teaching room (Figure 11). They were later transferred to the museum. As in these illustrations, Lockhart made use of colour to aid comprehension in the lecture-theatre and museum displays he coordinated. A late nineteenth-century plaster cast, for instance, was painted to form a colourful dermatome model (Figure 12).

The anatomy museum was transformed during the late 1960s under the direction of David Sinclair, appointed as professor of anatomy in 1964. With the reduction in time allocated for dissection within the medical curriculum in Britain there was increased need for efficient teaching methods.[17] In this context the museum was reconfigured so that learning both within it and within the dissecting room was more explicitly

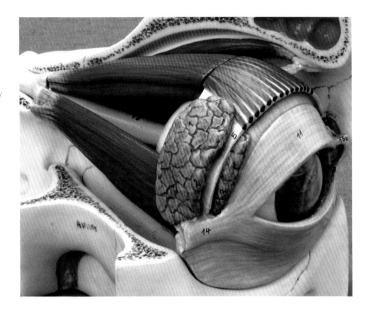

mutually reinforcing. Displays were focused primarily on human anatomy, with the relocation of comparative anatomy specimens, especially large skeletons, to the zoology museum (Figure 13). Human skulls from different parts of the world, especially those with original markings and modifications, such as the application of clay, were sent to the anthropological museum. These were now deemed more relevant to the study of human culture than of anatomy.

Old display cases were removed and specimens transferred from glass to transparent Perspex® in this refashioning of the museum using preferred 'modern' materials. The ground floor of the museum was divided into bays that displayed anatomical regions of the human body – the very regions that were explored in the dissecting room: upper limb, lower limb, thorax, abdomen, and head and neck (in addition to bays exhibiting neuroanatomy, and embryology). Students examined these anatomical regions within the open-shelved museum, in coordination with their exploration of bodies through dissection. Arranged in this way, the museum aided students in seeing how anatomical 'parts' linked up to form a 'whole body', especially as dissecting-

room bodies were progressively dismantled.[18] Museum objects considered irrelevant within this scheme were categorised as 'historical' and went into storage, while an installation on the upper gallery told a history of anatomy in Aberdeen, thereby distinguishing past from present anatomical practices.

The museum's general layout as an anatomical body was maintained for some 40 years (Figure 14). Yet changes were still unfolding within it. The practice of preserving human specimens from dissecting-room bodies declined after the mid 1960s. This cessation coincided with Sinclair's work to establish a memorial, built in the early 1970s at Trinity Cemetery in Aberdeen, dedicated to the local people who donate their bodies for anatomical examination. (Under current legislation, preserved parts of dissected bodies are only retained beyond three years with donors' written consent). Later, at the museum, several computers were incorporated into two of the bays for students to view anatomy software. Further additions to the museum

FIGURE 16 (ABOVE, LEFT)
The anatomy museum at Marischal College, vacated and internally re-configured as a temporary architectural construction and demolition planning office, 2010.
Photograph by Elizabeth Hallam.

FIGURE 17 (ABOVE, RIGHT)
Anatomy Resource Centre in the Anatomy Facility, Suttie Centre, School of Medicine and Dentistry, University of Aberdeen, 2010.
Photograph by Elizabeth Hallam.

continued when new sets of plastic anatomical models were purchased in the 1990s and early 2000s. Designed for handling, these were selected to complement and extend existing teaching materials (Figure 15).

REOPENING

October 2009: The contents of the anatomy museum and store, approximately 1,800 items, had been transported to the new anatomy facility in the Suttie Centre, near the medical school at Foresterhill. The last of Marischal College's medical museums was now empty, leaving only the anthropological museum. The latter (renamed Marischal Museum in 1990) had been closed to the public in 2008. Three years later exhibitions based on its collections were located at the new King's Museum in Old Aberdeen. With much of the college's long-vacated labyrinthine spaces reaching dereliction in 2009, two-thirds of the building was leased to the city council to house their headquarters. The anatomy museum became a temporary architectural planning office (Figure 16): here, workers coordinated the demolition of the college's old interior and its reconstruction as office accommodation, leaving the original massive granite façade in place.

At the anatomy facility, selected specimens and models from what was renamed the 'Anatomy Museum Collection' were re-installed (or stored) in the 'Anatomy Resource Centre' (Figure 17). Echoes of the anatomy museum persist, however, in the arrangement of bays and in the materials on shelves. Separated from its old architecture, the museum has become a collection: a resource for constant re-arranging, according to the requirements of present-day teaching; one that is still growing, with additions such as the models collaboratively designed and made on site by anatomy teaching staff, a technician and students (Figure 18).

Six medical museums (of anatomy, materia medica, medical jurisprudence/hygiene, midwifery, pathology, and surgery)

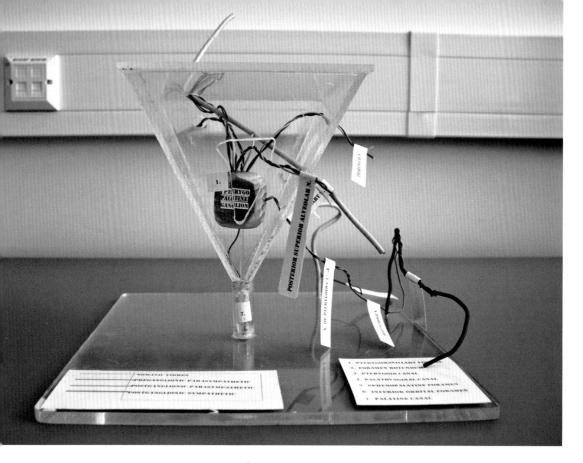

FIGURE 18
Model of the pterygopalatine ganglion
or nerve centre (an anatomical part
located under the cheekbone). Made
in the anatomy department, Marischal
College, University of Aberdeen, 2008.
Photograph by Elizabeth Hallam.

have thus become two collections (of pathology and forensic medicine, and of anatomy) – the latter with a room for display – that is still informally referred to by staff as the 'museum'. The complex factors involved in this process of disappearance and transformation are manifold, and this story touches on just a few: the politics of collecting, the institutional organisation of spaces, the changing practice of medicine, shifting attitudes to the body, developments both in teaching methods and in visual imaging technologies. Disappearance is here a process that entails not only material decay but also power, finance, ambition, failure, creativity.

NOTES

1. Jennifer Carter and Colin A McLaren, *Crown and Gown, 1495–1995: An Illustrated History of the University of Aberdeen* (Aberdeen: Aberdeen University Press, 1994).

2. Robert Walker and Alexander Macdonald Munro, *University of Aberdeen Quatercentenary Celebrations, September, 1906: Handbook to City and University* (Aberdeen: Aberdeen University Press, 1906); *Record of the*

Celebration of the Quatercentenary of the University of Aberdeen from the 25th to 28th September, 1906, ed. by P J Anderson (Aberdeen: Aberdeen University Press, 1907).

3. Walker and Munro, *University of Aberdeen,* p.101.

4. Robert W Reid, 'Presidential Address at the Ordinary Meeting', *University of Aberdeen Proceedings of the Anatomical and Anthropological Society, 1899–1900* (Aberdeen: Aberdeen University Press, 1900), pp. 6–15 (p. 15); Robert W Reid, *Illustrated Catalogue of the Anthropological Museum: University of Aberdeen* (Aberdeen: Aberdeen University Press, 1912). Helen Southwood, 'A Cultural History of Marischal Anthropological Museum in the Twentieth Century' (PhD thesis, University of Aberdeen, 2003).

5. Walker and Munro, *University of Aberdeen,* p. 103.

6. Report by Museum Committee (RMC), University of Aberdeen, 1905–06, Marischal Museum Archive (MMA). See Carolyn Pennington, *The Modernisation of Medical Teaching at Aberdeen in the Nineteenth Century* (Aberdeen: Aberdeen University Press, 1994).

7. Walker and Munro, *University of Aberdeen*; RMC, University of Aberdeen, 1904–05, 1906–07, 1908–09, MMA.

8. Register of bodies brought to the Parochial Burying House, Aberdeen, 1843–1944, Special Libraries and Archives (SLA), University of Aberdeen; Elizabeth Hallam, *Anatomy Museum: Death and the Body Displayed* (London: Reaktion Books, forthcoming 2014).

9. Reid, 'Presidential Address', pp. 14, 13.

10. Catalogue of Preparations, Instruments, etc. in the Surgery Department, 1882–1923, SLA, University of Aberdeen.

11. Walker and Munro, *University of Aberdeen*, p. 71. 'The New Medical School at Aberdeen', *The Lancet*, 2 (1938), 803; CJ Hackett, 'A List of Medical Museums of Great Britain (1949–50)', *British Medical Journal*, 1 (1951), 1380–83.

12. www.abdn.ac.uk/historic/museums/pathology.

13. Robert D Lockhart, Application, 1938; Aberdeen: New Medical School: Preliminary figures, 1930s–1950s, SLA, University of Aberdeen.

14. 'Future of the Medical Museum', *The Lancet*, 1 (1945), 376–7; Jonathan Reinarz, 'The Age of Museum Medicine: The Rise and Fall of the Medical Museum at Birmingham's School of Medicine', *Social History of Medicine*, 18 (2005), 419–37; Samuel JMM Alberti, *Morbid Curiosities: Medical Museums in Nineteenth-Century Britain* (Oxford: Oxford University Press, 2011).

15. See Southwood, 'A Cultural History'.

16. Robert D Lockhart, *Living Anatomy: A Photographic Atlas of Muscles in Action and Surface Contours* (London: Faber and Faber, 1948).

17. David Sinclair, *A Student's Guide to Anatomy* (Oxford: Blackwell, 1961).

18. Sinclair, *A Student's Guide.* p. 21.

19. http://abdn.ac.uk/library/about/kings-museum.

Medicine at the Science Museum, London

Robert Bud

The medical collection at the Science Museum in London, built up from the 1970s, was one of the first to be a major part of a national museum of science and industry. With just a few exceptions, such as the Boerhaave in the Netherlands, most such museums, including the Musée des Arts et Métiers in Paris and the Deutsches Museum in Munich, had excluded medicine. Rather than developing as part of science museums, great medical collections had instead tended to develop within natural history and botany collections, in medical schools and in private collections such as the huge museum established in London during the early twentieth century by the industrialist and philanthropist Henry Wellcome (1853–1936). This chapter explores the Wellcome Trust collection – which ranks among the largest material resources for the history of medicine – focusing on its history, its meaning and its transfer to the Science Museum where it has been interpreted for public display.

EXHIBITING MEDICINE

Henry Wellcome's vision was nothing less than a history of humanity recorded through people's attitudes to health, medicine and disease.[1] The list of sections in the Wellcome Historical Medical Museum, which opened in 1913 and required full-time assistants, is indicative: 'prehistoric archaeology,

classical archaeology, antiquities, folklore, ethnology, and racial development with physical anthropology'.[2] Innumerable artefacts accumulated in one of the world's greatest collections.[3] When Wellcome died in 1936, his company, fortune and collections of books and artefacts became the responsibility of the Wellcome Trust. In the mid-1960s the governors decided to rationalise the collections.[4] Books and archives stayed with the magnificent Wellcome Library but many of the objects, generally defined as ethnographic or archaeological rather than medico-historical, were loaned, sold or donated to appropriate museums. For instance, Native American material was donated to the Museum of Cultural History (now the Fowler Museum) at the University of California, Los Angeles.[5] The remaining 100,000 items of special interest for the history of medicine were loaned to the Science Museum (where the collection remains on permanent loan). The process of transfer from the Wellcome store to the Science Museum, beginning in 1977, was gradual owing to the required cataloguing of material, much of which had scant previous documentation.[6] As a result of this acquisition, the Science Museum became a leader in the interpretation of how significant biomedicine was to twentieth-century science and technology.

The collection inherited by the Science Museum was encyclopaedic. Internationally significant groups of maiolica pharmacyware, microscopes, pestles and mortars, wooden saints and even samples of tattooed skin came to a museum that had previously been far more focused on the laboratories and factories of famous scientists and technologists (Figure 1).

At the Science Museum, the finest items in the collection were displayed in two large exhibitions that, with some modifications, remain in place at the time of writing. One is intended to appeal to interested adults, the other is more family-oriented. The former, *The Science and Art of Medicine*, includes 5,000 items shown in a huge display of 532 showcases. Opened in 1981, it draws on the history of medicine (as it had developed to the time of the exhibition's launch), including a chronological

FIGURE 2 (OPPOSITE)
Model showing childbirth during the 1860s, in *Glimpses of Medical History* at the Science Museum, 2012.
Science Museum/Science and Society Picture Library.

FIGURE 3 (ABOVE)
Folding parturition chair, German, 1780–1850.
Science Museum/Science and Society Picture Library.

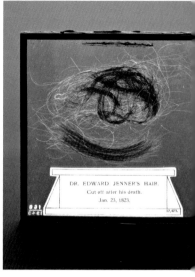

interpretation of doctors' tools and craft up to 1800, and displays of the period defined as 'modern medicine', which take the story up to the present, addressing subjects including dentistry, ophthalmology, physiology, microbiology, pharmacology and surgery. On the floor below, in *Glimpses of Medical History*, the subject is interpreted through room sets and dioramas, several from the Wellcome Historical Medical Museum, showing patients and doctors together from the neolithic to the present (Figure 2).

COLLECTING MEDICINE

The exhibitions serve as a fitting and impressive setting that provides public access to significant artefacts collected by Henry Wellcome and his active assistants, such as Peter Johnston-Saint, Wellcome's principal collector in Europe. Originally, Wellcome's collection was built up in two quite different ways. For the period before 1880, Wellcome accumulated objects that could be displayed to provide insights into social history.[7] A century later, this approach was seen to complement the social orientation of the history of medicine as a university discipline, which informed displays at the Science Museum. For example, objects from the collection illustrating social life from birth

to death could be displayed in the form of birthing furniture (Figure 3), early nineteenth-century mortsafes used to prevent grave robbing (Figure 4) and locks of hair taken after a person's death, often to act as reminders of the deceased (Figure 5).

However, Wellcome had treated the period from 1880 onwards as that of a 'modern' age and as the stage for a series of great pioneers including Louis Pasteur and Joseph Lister, rather than as a 'historical' period to be collected (Figure 6). So although some medicine chests of celebrity explorers, for instance, were included in his collection, artefacts from the work of his own company's laboratories were scarce. After Wellcome's death in 1936 acquisitions slowed to a trickle but these nevertheless featured a few fascinating items. For example, a model of an ideal hospital, whose construction had been sponsored by the King's Fund Hospital Trust in 1931 to invigorate the design of modern facilities in Britain, was acquired in 1958 (Figure 7). Yet the emerging era of molecular biomedicine was not adequately represented by these acquisitions.

Because the Wellcome Trust collection hardly reflected such key medical developments taking place during the twentieth century, Science Museum staff had to supplement it by acquiring

FIGURE 6 (LEFT)
Compound monocular microscope, 1861–1870, belonging to Pasteur, collected by Henry Wellcome.
Science Museum/Science and Society Picture Library.

FIGURE 7 (RIGHT)
Children's ward, King Edward VII Hospital Fund model, 1932.
Science Museum/Science and Society Picture Library.

further artefacts, in addition to documenting and conserving the collection. They mixed established Science Museum approaches to documenting major steps in medical practice with the social-historical emphasis of the Wellcome Historical Medical Museum. A modern heart surgery unit was acquired, as well as pioneering scanners (Figure 8). Major sets of objects relating to twentieth-century microbiology, pharmaceuticals, surgery, anaesthesiology, radiology and dentistry were also collected.

CHANGING GALLERIES

In 1994, the Science Museum opened an additional gallery devoted to twentieth-century medicine entitled *Heath Matters*.[8] Recently updated, its three sections deal respectively with the rise of medicine and the technology of the modern hospital, populations and health, and medical research (Figure 9). Rather than exhibiting the evolution of objects over time, or aiming for encyclopaedic coverage of an issue – as in earlier museum displays – this gallery exhibits diverse objects to explore aspects of their social and technical construction. For example, an exhibit relating to Lord Nuffield's donation of iron lungs (which had been offered to every hospital in the British Empire in 1938) explains how this object is both a medical device, and a bricolage – that is, an assembly of various components, some from Nuffield's under-employed car factories. The Science Museum well understands too that objects alone are but one means of communication with its visitors. So archive materials, original newsreels of the iron lung and interactive exhibits, encouraging visitors to share their ideas on the nature of health, are used in the exhibition.

In the Wellcome Wing of the Science Museum, with the end of the millennium approaching, a new display dealing with contemporary science, technology and medicine was erected. One floor uses objects to present a contemporary view entitled *Who am I?*, and is largely devoted to contemporary genetics

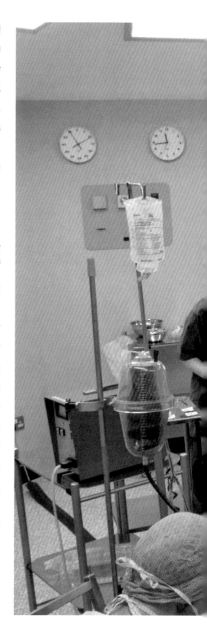

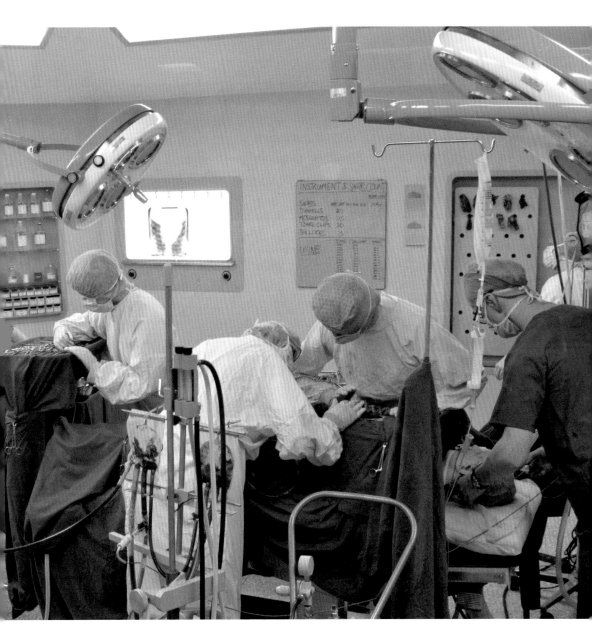

FIGURE 8
Life-size reconstruction of an
operating theatre dating from the
1980s, with models of surgeons
performing heart surgery.
Science Museum/Science and
Society Picture Library.

FIGURE 9
The rise of medicine section in *Health
Matters* at the Science Museum, 2012.
Science Museum/Science and
Society Picture Library.

and issues of inheritance and neuroscience. This exhibition
demonstrates the long-term Science Museum approach of
presenting contemporary science and technology for its visitors,
using many medical objects as well as interactive exhibits to
do so. Because it is 'contemporary' and therefore expected
to be up-to-date, it was refurbished in 2010 to take account of
new knowledge and interests and to allow for future updates. It
includes, for instance, art commissions and purchases offering
new perspectives, and is informed by the sci-art movement,
which uses art to communicate science in an alternative manner.
It has been generally supported by the Wellcome Trust itself. The
exhibition is complemented by the adjacent historical treatment
of science, technology and medicine, in *Making the Modern World*,
which displays important medical artefacts (Figure 10).

While these exhibits address biomedicine, the collections
inherited by the Science Museum are also rich in materials from

healthcare practices associated with non-Western traditions. Many aspects of these are displayed in *The Science and Art of Medicine* exhibition. In the past few years the Science Museum has been reaching out more than ever before to its audiences, especially by tailoring exhibitions to their interests. As many lay visitors value complementary medicine, a new exhibition looks at Ayurvedic, Chinese, Unani Tibb and African traditions in their indigenous environments and as practiced in the West. Diverse visitor responses to the exhibition indicate people's commitments to biomedicine, which some see as the only effective source of cures, as well as personal beliefs in the efficacy of different medical traditions (Figure 11).

Significantly, attitudes to the peoples from whom the collection was drawn have changed radically since the period when Wellcome built up his collection within an imperial context. The most challenging aspect of this change has been the storage and display of human remains. When the Science

FIGURE 10
Penicillium mould from Professor Alexander Fleming, 1935. Science Museum/Science and Society Picture Library.

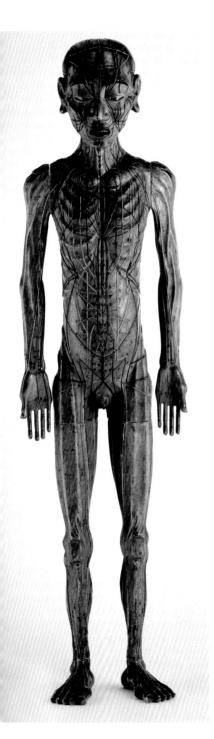

Museum acquired the collection in the 1970s this was not yet seen by museums as a prominent issue. By the turn of the twenty-first century, however, values had changed decisively, shaped by public debate. With close cooperation of the Wellcome Trust governors, a new human remains policy has been developed at the Science Museum to guide the appropriate and respectful storage, treatment and display of approximately 800 human remains and objects incorporating human remains.[9] Some human remains have been returned to the indigenous communities from which they originated – for example, in 2006 three skulls believed to be of Australian Aboriginal origin were repatriated, as was a Hawaiian skull in 2012.

UNPACKING OBJECTS

Rich as they are, the Science Museum permanent displays interpret only a very small proportion of the medical collections it holds, owing to constraints on exhibition space. Even in the late 1980s, many of the artefacts from Henry Wellcome's collection were still in their original crates. During 1994 to 1995 every object was examined, conserved if necessary and laid out in a newly fitted-out storage facility at Blythe House in West Kensington, four kilometres from the Science Museum, where they can be examined by appointment and drawn upon by curators. Arranging loans to other museums, such as the Deutsches Hygiene-Museum's major temporary exhibitions and particularly to the Wellcome Trust's displays at Wellcome Collection on Euston Road, London (see Arnold and Chaplin in this volume), has become a major opportunity and responsibility. In addition, the Science Museum has provided access to collections through its own temporary exhibitions. These have encouraged the public to view otherwise hidden objects and to rethink attitudes to medicine. The topics on display, ranging from public health to psychoanalysis, have explored such issues as medical treatment, the responsibilities of patients, and the nature of the mind (Figure 12).

The Science Museum continues to collect objects but often these have only been stored, not displayed (Figure 13). The internet, however, offers new possibilities for communication and for engaging with the public. The Science Museum currently presents 4,000 items from the collection on a website entitled *Brought to Life: Exploring the History of Medicine*, an initiative supported by the Wellcome Trust.[10] This website focuses on museum objects to offer a broader interpretation of the history of medicine. It is aimed at high school students and medical students pursuing the history of medicine, as well as a wider audience. Images of objects and historical interpretations of their significance are complemented on the one hand by thematic essays and useful references and, on the other, by interactive exhibits that are intended to be both fun and informative. The images are made available on a creative-commons-type licence, which permits free reuse with attribution. The website, completed in 2010, presents as many objects as a major exhibition. With almost 700,000 visits a year, 37% from each of the UK and US, and 17% from continental Europe, it has also attracted visitors in numbers equivalent to a major museum. The web is therefore a powerful and attractive way of publishing museum images and stories.

Developments at the Science Museum during the past thirty years reflect greater awareness of the importance of visitors and the diverse voices and points of view of patients. These are informing the museum as it renews its interpretation of the medical collection for the twenty-first century. A fascinating new use of the 1980s operating theatre, on display in the museum, has developed through collaboration with neighbouring Imperial College London. It is used not only to show medical students how operations prior to keyhole surgery were conducted but also to engage members of the public who can see simulated operations and ask questions.

Such activities keep the collection alive. Developments in digital technology and the engagement of active audiences – for whom medicine as an institution, profession and industry looms

FIGURE 11 (OPPOSITE)
Acupuncture figure, Chinese, late Ming dynasty, 17th century.
Science Museum/Science and Society Picture Library.

FIGURE 12 (ABOVE)
Facial votive displayed in the exhibition *Psychoanalysis: The Unconscious in Everyday Life*, held October 2010–April 2011, which helped visitors explore the workings of the unconscious mind through a range of modern and historical objects and contemporary artworks.
Science Museum/Science and Society Picture Library.

ever larger – are central considerations for the Science Museum. It is vital to appreciate that whether online or in person, museum visitors are also lay consumers of medicine. The interests of families eager for education count at the museum as well as those of health professionals and students. Planning the Science Museum's new acquisitions in this context is a major challenge, as is the question of how the now thirty-year-old medical displays are to be re-thought for the twenty-first century so that they are authoritative yet provide space for diverse visitors' and patients' perspectives. These are urgent and current issues.

FIGURE 13
'Jedi' helmets for magnetic resonance imaging (MRI) of the brain, 1984. To take MRI scans of the brain, these helmets were worn by children and adults. The coils are aerials for picking up MRI signals. Naming them after the Jedi knights in Star Wars® films encouraged children to put them on and not to be frightened of the procedure. Science Museum/Science and Society Picture Library.

NOTES

1. Ghislaine Skinner, 'Sir Henry Wellcome's Museum for the Science of History, *Medical History*, 30 (1986), pp. 383–418.

2. Quoted in Skinner, 'Sir Henry Wellcome's Museum', p. 398.

3. Frances Larson, *An Infinity of Things: How Sir Henry Wellcome Collected the World* (Oxford: Oxford University Press, 2009).

4. A Rupert Hall and BA Bembridge, *Physic and Philanthropy: A History of the Wellcome Trust, 1936–1986* (Cambridge: Cambridge University Press, 1986), pp. 131–145.

5. G Russell, 'The Wellcome Historical Medical Museum's Dispersal of Nonmedical Material, 1936–1983', *Museums Journal*, 62 (1986), supplement S3–29; Jude Hill, 'Travelling Objects: the Wellcome Collection in Los Angeles, London and Beyond', *Cultural Geographies*, 13 (2006), pp. 340–366.

6. John Burnett, 'Cataloguing the Wellcome Collection', in *Proceedings of the Second Symposium of the European Association of Museums of the History of Medical Sciences* ed. by Brian Bracegridle (Paris: Fondation Marcel Merieux, 1984), pp. 25–27.

7. Skinner, 'Sir Henry Wellcome's Museum', p. 406.

8. Timothy M Boon, 'Histories, Exhibitions, Collections: Reflections on the Language of Medical Curatorship at the Science Museum after Health Matters', in *Manifesting Medicine*, ed. by Robert Bud, 2nd edn (London: NMSI trading, second edition, 2004), pp. 123–143.

9. The Human Remains Policy is at www.sciencemuseum.org.uk.

10. www.sciencemuseum.org.uk/broughttolife.

8   720

Recycling anatomical preparations

Leiden's anatomical collections

Marieke Hendriksen, Hieke Huistra and Rina Knoeff

This chapter explores anatomical preparations in the Leiden University Anatomical Collections. The notion of recycling here helps us understand how preparations have been adapted for different purposes over time. Firstly, we look at the original intentions behind the preparations made by the famous anatomist Bernard Siegfried Albinus. We then discuss how the preparations were used in the nineteenth century for research and teaching purposes. Finally, we consider the present collections at Leiden as an example of how recycling promotes the survival and future use of anatomical preparations.

The Leiden anatomical collections are the oldest of their kind in Europe. From the sixteenth century onwards the anatomical theatre with its many exhibits, housed in the Faliedebagijnkerk, one of the town's churches, was an important crowd puller. The theatre served not only as an important tourist site, and a storage space for all kinds of curious objects but also as a signpost for the excellence of research in Leiden as, in this public place, many medical controversies were battled out (Figure 1).[1]

IMAGE
Detail from Figure 4.

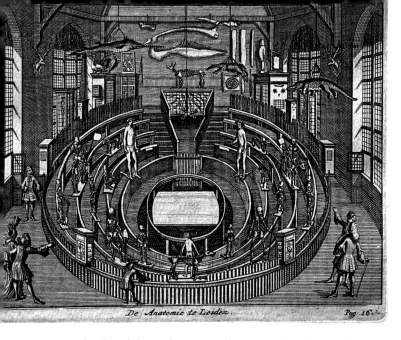

FIGURE 1
The Leiden Anatomical Theatre,
depicted in P van der Aa, *Les Délices
de Leyde* (Leiden: P van der Aa, 1712).
Museum Boerhaave, Leiden.

In the eighteenth century, however, the theatre became obsolete as a place for medical and anatomical research. Anatomy professor Bernard Siegfried Albinus (1697–1770) moved away from the theatre's tourist business and started building his own collections in a private room adjacent to the theatre (Figure 2).[2] Albinus is considered a founding figure of the Leiden collections and in subsequent historical periods his collections have remained central to the Leiden anatomical museum (Figure 3).

Yet, for the Albinus collections to remain relevant over time, they had to be recycled. This means they were subject to reinterpretation, reuse and reordering according to prevailing medical and anatomical opinions. The Albinus preparations show par excellence how collections are fluid and how, through recycling, they have been continuously adapted to current fields of knowledge and expertise, as well as to the financial, educational and other circumstances so crucial for the custody of collections.

ELEGANT ANATOMY

Albinus made most of his famous preparations in the first half of the eighteenth century. In his work he strove not only to make anatomical knowledge but also to represent the ideal body.[3] So, in answering contemporary questions relating to medicine,

Albinus was also intent on showing the perfection and elegance of human anatomy. He stressed the hands-on importance of the microscope and the use of syringes to inject blood vessels, not only in the search for knowledge about the vascular system but also for making perfect, life-like preparations. By doing so, Albinus became a master of transformation, making products of the dissection room into elegant preparations. The Swiss anatomist Albrecht von Haller praised such skill, noting that when Albinus conducted anatomical demonstrations he never even soiled the sleeves of his coat!

Looking closely at his preparations reveals how Albinus combined his ideas about anatomical knowledge and bodily perfection. A child's arm was injected with red wax to make it appear life-like (Figure 4). It is decorated with a lace-trimmed

FIGURE 2 (LEFT)
Portrait of Albinus. Print by
JJ Haid and CI de Moor, 1741.
Universiteitsbibliotheek, Leiden.

FIGURE 3 (RIGHT)
The Albinus brothers in their
cabinet, depicted in FB Albinus,
Supellex Anatomica (Leiden:
Petrum Delfos, 1775).
Universiteitsbibliotheek, Leiden.

sleeve holding the choroid membrane (a thin film of tissue in the eye) on a string. Another preparation – the skin from a hand of a four-month-old foetus – although now almost disintegrated, was originally made to look like a glove, hanging from a sprig of the plant *Aster Africanus* or *Senecio elegans* (Figures 5 and 6). These preparations were evidence of Albinus as a champion of elegant anatomy, for hardly anything is more difficult than injecting and preparing such delicate structures as eye or skin membranes.

Moreover, the preparations are testimony to the notion that the hand is the anatomist's most important tool, the instrument of instruments. But the hand would be lost without the eye. Sight was considered the highest and most reliable sense, which was hugely important in making anatomical knowledge. So Albinus's preparations had multiple meanings: they were about the anatomical structures of the hand and the eye as much as the senses of touch and sight. They were also demonstrations of how to prepare the skin and eye elegantly as well as allegorical references to the anatomist's two most important senses.

Although Albinus's preparations were housed at the university, they remained his private property. When he died, his widow auctioned the collection as a whole, and the university purchased it for the hefty sum of 6,300 guilders (equivalent to €60,000 in 2012). From a letter written in 1771 by the new professor of medicine, Wouter van Doeveren, it appears that the purchase was as much about prestige as it was about the usefulness of the collection. He complained that public esteem for the Albinus collection was too high and that it would have made at least a thousand guilders less had it been broken up and sold separately. With the development of pathological anatomy, the teaching of pathology aided by preparations became increasingly important. Van Doeveren's irritation was probably aroused by the fact that this new pathology teaching of deformed and diseased anatomy was not very well served by Albinus's collection of perfect, supposedly 'normal' anatomy.

FIGURE 4 (ABOVE)
Wet preparation by Bernhard Siegfried Albinus. The child's arm has a lace-trimmed sleeve, and is holding a choroid membrane injected with red wax.
Photograph © Anatomisch Museum Leiden University Medical Center, 2012.

FIGURE 5 (OPPOSITE)
Wet preparation by Bernhard Siegfried Albinus. The entire epidermis of a child's hand was removed from the hand like a glove. It was tied and hung from a sprig of *Aster Africanus*. The epidermis is now on the bottom of the glass phial.
Photograph by Arno Massee.
© Anatomisch Museum Leiden University Medical Center, 2012.

At the request of the university governors, Albinus's younger brother, Frederik, together with professor Eduard Sandifort, wrote a report on the best way to house and use the newly acquired Albinus collection, advising that the dilapidated anatomical theatre should be restructured and redecorated. In the newly decorated theatre, the Albinus collection remained a showpiece for the remainder of the eighteenth century.[4] And its keepers were perhaps even more protective of the collections than Albinus himself had been. Indeed, the English botanist James Edward Smith implied that Sandifort was a little overprotective. He wrote in 1786:

> Professor Sandifort shewed me the Anatomical Theatre, and the preparations of Albinus; the latter can be seen in his presence only. Among them are some fine things, particularly the preparations relating to the progress of ossification in the foetus, a favourite subject of Albinus; but on the whole this collection will bear no comparison with either of the Hunterian Museums.[5] (See Alberti in this volume.)

Yet, despite Sandifort's protectionist efforts, the Albinus collections would soon be recycled in order to serve the nineteenth-century needs of the Leiden medical faculty.

FIGURE 6
Senecio elegans. Colour print from Curtis, *The Botanical Magazine,* 1792, vol 7, no 238. Naturalis Biodiversity Center, National Herbarium of the Netherlands, Leiden.

LABORATORY AND TEACHING PREPARATIONS

In the nineteenth century the Leiden anatomical collections underwent far-reaching changes, which affected even the conservation and preservation of preparations. They were moved to a different site in Leiden, adjacent to the university's laboratories, and largely closed to the public. The collections, in other words, were recycled from public hotspots into research and teaching objects.[6]

This had important consequences for the Albinus collections, as is evident in the changing designs of the catalogues relating to these objects. At the turn of the eighteenth century Sandifort had catalogued Albinus's preparations (together with the collections of Leiden anatomists Johannes

Rau and Wouter van Doeveren) in two large published volumes, the *Museum Anatomicum* (1793). Sandifort's catalogue was beautifully illustrated and much sought after – it can still be found in libraries across Europe. A century later, in 1892, the preparations were catalogued again. This time the outcome was a small manuscript book without illustrations, two copies of which are held at the Leiden University archive. In barely a century, the collections had been withdrawn into the medical faculty, accessible only to Leiden medical researchers and students. The Leiden anatomical collections were no longer a public attraction, lay audiences having been successfully removed from the museum.

Nineteenth-century political decisions were crucial in this changing management of the collections. Educational reforms, in particular, transformed the Albinus collections. In the first half of the century they became status objects in the hands of university governors. In later years students and professors used them in response to specific nineteenth-century laboratory-based research questions and in hands-on teaching, as did anatomy teacher Teunis Zaaijer (Figure 7).

The Royal Decree on Higher Education (1815) ruled that medical faculties must teach comparative anatomy and pathology as distinctly different disciplines, when previously these disciplines had been part of the broader field of anatomy. Moreover – and even King William I himself was involved in this decision – the decree ordered that the new disciplines must be supported by the material kept in the collections. To the horror of Leiden governors other universities in the Netherlands had also begun to acquire anatomical collections, thereby eroding Leiden's boast of being the best Dutch university. The university governors reacted swiftly: they took the beautiful Albinus preparations and turned them into promotional objects, marketing Leiden's glorious past and its continued superiority in anatomical teaching.

FIGURE 7
Teunis Zaaijer in the lecture hall, using objects from the collections, around 1890.
Museum Boerhaave, Leiden.

FIGURE 8
The teaching laboratory for
physics, chemistry and anatomy,
which housed the anatomical
collections from 1860 onwards.
Photograph by J Goedeljee and Ad. Braun,
1866. Beeldbank, Regionaal Archief Leiden.

The cunning strategy worked, but only until the 1860s when a second educational reform initiated the setting up of teaching laboratories. The collections were relocated from the Faliedebagijnkerk to a purpose-built educational complex with laboratories of physics, chemistry and physiology (Figure 8). These 'laboratory collections' were much less accessible to lay visitors than the anatomical theatre had been before. They were not only further removed from the city centre but also located in restricted-access laboratories where they were regulated by specific rules. The number of visitors to the collections dropped sharply, especially as they were no longer a tourist attraction. Whereas the early modern theatre attracted many lay visitors, the number dropped to between twenty and forty people each year in the early 1860s. And after 1865 an average of four visitors per annum came to see the collections.

The move to the laboratory space also had important consequences for many Albinus preparations. Most important was that the name of Albinus was no longer attached to them – the same happened to other specimens in the Leiden collections, which were likewise orphaned. Consequently, they could no longer be used as status symbols. Instead the Albinus preparations were reinterpreted in terms of teaching and research. A good example of this is preparation 'Ab0189', a skull originally prepared by Albinus (Figure 9). In 1902, a medical student used the skull for his doctoral research on the malformation of teeth but he no longer related the preparation to Albinus. The preparation had shifted from being an 'Albinus piece' in Sandifort's 1793 catalogue, into an anonymous part of a collection of '22 dry preparations' in the catalogue of 1892 – a preparation that could easily be re-used in new research projects. This, of course, does not mean that all of the precious Albinus preparations were reinterpreted. It does, however, indicate that the preparations acquired new and different meanings with every educational reform, according to the whims of governors or simply as a result of relocation to a different building.

THE FUTURE OF (ALBINUS'S) PREPARATIONS

The twenty-first century has seen the Leiden anatomical collections relocated again and the Albinus preparations

FIGURE 9
Stereographic photograph of a skull from the Albinus collection, depicted in AL Erkelens, *Rententio Dentium* (Leiden: IJdo, 1902). Universiteitsbibliotheek, Leiden.

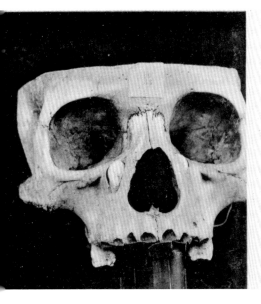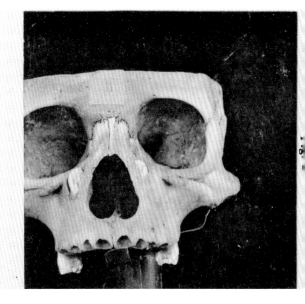

FIGURE 10
The Albinus cabinet at the
Anatomical Museum.
Photograph by Hieke Huistra.
© Anatomisch Museum Leiden
University Medical Center, 2012.

(presented in an eighteenth-century style within their original
cabinet) now take pride of place in the new Anatomical Museum
at the Leiden University Medical Center (LUMC) (Figure 10).
Although the public visiting hours remain rather restricted to
two weekends per year, medical students and school classes
can make an appointment at any time. Albinus appears to
have become even more of a key historical figure at the Leiden
medical faculty. On the outside wall, adjacent to the entrance, a
huge poster of an engraving from Albinus's famous anatomical
atlas is like a sign indicating the entrance to the building. It is
accompanied by the text 'non scholae sed vitae discimus', originally
from Seneca, the Roman writer, meaning: we do not learn just
for school, but for life (Figure 11). Albinus's new role – which is
reminiscent of the nineteenth-century governors' efforts – is to

point to the rich history of the Leiden faculty and the continued excellence of the medical curriculum.

Recycling anatomical preparations has been important in the survival of anatomical collections, and could be a way to save collections in the future. Recent teaching methods in medicine – and particularly a decline in practical anatomy – have caused many collections to become obsolete and underappreciated. Moreover, financial constraints and crises have easily led to a de-prioritisation of funding for the conservation, storage and sometimes even the preservation of anatomical collections. As a result, collections worldwide have come under threat when consigned to damp cellars and stuffy attics (see Hallam and Alberti in this volume). Part of the Leiden collections suffered the same fate and, because of a severe lack of

FIGURE 11
Entrance of the Leiden
University Faculty of Medicine
with the Albinus poster.
Photograph by Hieke Huistra, 2012.

FIGURE 13
Postcard with Leiden University
students surrounded by the
anatomical collections, around 1990.

storage space, some preparations even ended up in the worst unacclimatised circumstances.

Luckily the LUMC embraces the task of caring for Leiden's anatomical past. In the new Anatomical Museum the old collections have been cleverly integrated into the medical curriculum (Figures 12 and 13). Old preparations have been relocated, restored, redisplayed and redefined in terms of new medical teaching – for example, teaching on the life cycle, and a whole floor is dedicated to the exhibition of historical preparations and rarities. Displayed alongside preparations defined as 'relevant' teaching material are also bottles with beaded babies, eighteenth-century sailors' tattoos, bladder stones, monstrous births and lace-embellished infants' heads (Figure 14). For anatomical collections it is of vital importance to ensure that recycling has a future. Recognising that preparations have multiple and changing meanings and uses might encourage their continued reuse, thereby helping to protect the material remains of anatomy's past.

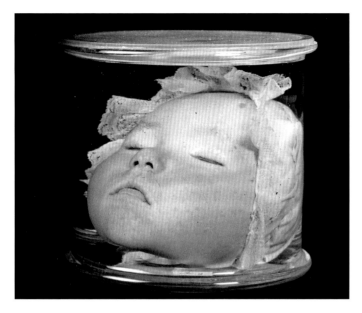

FIGURE 14
Wet preparation by Frederik
Ruysch. A lace-decorated infant's
head. © Anatomisch Museum Leiden
University Medical Center, 2012.

NOTES

1. Tim Huisman, *The Finger of God. Anatomical Practice in Seventeenth-Century Leiden* (Leiden: Primavera Press, 2009); Rina Knoeff, 'The Visitor's View: Early Modern Tourism and the Polyvalence of Anatomical Exhibits', in *Centres and Cycles of Accumulation in and around the Netherlands during the Early Modern Period*, ed. by Lissa Roberts (Münster: LIT, 2011), pp. 155–76.

2. Hendrik Punt, *Bernard Siegfried Albinus (1697–1770), On 'Human Nature': Anatomical and Physiological Ideas in Eighteenth-Century Leiden* (University of Michigan: Israel, 1983).

3. Marieke Hendriksen, 'Aesthesis in Anatomy. Materiality and Elegance in the Eighteenth-Century Leiden Anatomical Collections' (PhD thesis, Leiden University, 2012).

4. AM Elshout, *Het Leidse Kabinet der Anatomie uit de achttiende eeuw. De betekenis van een wetenschappelijke collectie als cultuurhistorisch monument* (Leiden: University Press,1952).

5. James Edward Smith, *A Sketch of a Tour on the Continent, in the Years 1786 and 1787*, 3 vols (London, 1793), I, p. 15. Our italics.

6. Hieke Huistra, 'Preparations on the Move. The Leiden Anatomical Collections in the Nineteenth Century' (PhD thesis, Leiden University, 2013).

Anatomy and public enlightenment

The Florentine Museo 'La Specola'

Anna Maerker

Ant.º Donati del

1. Giardini Botanici
2. Stufa per le Piante
3. Specula Astronomica
4. Monas.º d'Anna Elena
5. Monas.º S. Chiara
6. Chiesa del Carmine
7. Conservatorio delle Salesiane

Veduta del Real Museo
dalla parte del Re

FIGURE 1
Royal Museum of Physics and
Natural History ('La Specola'),
Florence, around 1800.
Biblioteca Nazionale Centrale, Florence.

ica, e d'Istoria Naturale
ardino di Boboli

Aniello Lamberti inc.

8. Casino del Medici
9. Porta S. Frediano
10. Mura della Città
11. Villa Franceschi a bella Vista
12. Convento degl' Olivetani
13. Borgo al Pignone
14. Cascine

Travellers to Florence are faced with a wide choice of sights and sensations, from intricate, intensely coloured medieval mosaics to imposing sculptures of rulers past. Beyond the well-trodden paths of generations of Grand (or not so grand) Tourists, past the bustle of Ponte Vecchio and Palazzo Pitti, a spectacle of a very different nature awaits its visitors. Palazzo Torrigiani, on Via Romana adjacent to the Boboli Gardens, houses the zoological museum of the University of Florence, known as 'La Specola' (Figure 1). Here, one enters a cool courtyard and ascends the grooved steps worn down by centuries of visitors who have been to see the museum's collection of *naturalia*, from mineral samples and dried plants to animals, taxidermied or preserved in fluids (Figure 2). But La Specola offers more than the usual trappings of a provincial natural history museum: beyond the zoological specimens, the museum is home to a spectacular collection of anatomical wax models of human anatomy. This chapter recounts the models' role for the Tuscan Grand Duke's mission of public enlightenment, the conflicts between anatomists and artisans that plagued the process of model production at the museum's workshop, and the ways in which visitors responded to the spectacle of artificial anatomy.

The last ten rooms of the museum are filled with coloured, mostly life-size waxes. The models are presented in a variety of ways. In the centre of the room, entire male or female bodies recline on silk cushions, enclosed in elegant wooden showcases with glass panels that afford visibility from all sides (Figures 3 and 4). Those models are 'dissected' to make visible a particular aspect of the body – the nervous system, digestion, the muscles or the lymphatic system are laid bare to invite closer study. But they also include features that attract more emotional responses from visitors. The models, even those lacking skin, exhibit expressive faces and poses reminiscent of classical works of art. In some cases they include decorative details such as the long hair of the 'anatomical Venuses', reclining figures of women whose languid poses and relaxed, even joyful expressions seem at odds with their open torsos, which reveal the inner organs (Figures 5 and 6). Thus, the models appeal to visitors' aesthetic judgment and enjoyment, as much as to their desire to learn about the structure of the human body. The educational mission of the collection is reinforced further by additional materials. To enable a comprehensive vision of the body, a range of organs and fragments are presented in smaller showcases stacked around the walls, supplementing the central figure.[1] Diagrammatic drawings complete the panoramic vision, and refer the viewer to numbered lists of anatomical details (Figures 7 and 8).[2]

These anatomical waxes have been a feature of the Florentine landscape of spectacular sights since the late eighteenth century. Founded as the Royal Museum of Physics and Natural History in Florence in 1775, La Specola was an experiment in public enlightenment. The museum was one of the first science museums in Europe explicitly open to the general public, and a central element in Grand Duke Pietro Leopoldo's plan to turn his Tuscan subjects into civilised citizens through science education. In its original inception, the museum displayed natural and scientific objects, from minerals, plants and animals to physics instruments and chemical apparatus, and even came

FIGURE 2 (OPPOSITE)
Backstage at La Specola, Florence, 2007.
Photograph by Joanna Ebenstein, *Morbid Anatomy*.

FIGURE 3 (ABOVE)
Detail of a wax model, made around 1800, at La Specola, Florence.
Photograph by Tanya Marcuse, *Wax Bodies*, N°40, 2006.

FIGURE 4
Gallery at La Specola, 2007.
Photograph by Joanna
Ebenstein, *Morbid Anatomy.*

to include an astronomical observatory ('specola'), after which the museum as a whole was soon popularly known.

When Grand Duke Pietro Leopoldo of Habsburg-Lorraine (1747–1792) assumed power in Tuscany at the age of eighteen, he was determined to put to good use the education he had received at the Viennese court of his mother, Empress Maria Teresa. Steeped in the latest political, social and economic theories, Pietro Leopoldo was also a keen amateur scientist who enjoyed chemical experimentation. (His own chemistry cabinet is now on display at the Museo Galileo of the History of Science, just behind the Uffizi Art Gallery, Figure 9.) The young Grand Duke was convinced of the benefits of natural philosophical enquiry for political action. He was certain that 'a good legislation is like sound natural philosophy; it must be founded on experiment'.[3] Tuscany under his reign should become a political laboratory, he thought, a territory where reform measures could be explored under experimental conditions. But to make his subjects comply with such experiments, Tuscans needed science education. Local intellectuals shared and supported the sovereign's vision – a commentator in the journal *Novelle Letterarie* opined that 'governments and sovereigns have to promote and procure public education. The man who grows up ignorant [...] is always a bad citizen; [...] he does not serve the purpose to which the natural order has destined him'. Tuscans should be taught 'the science of order' to understand that 'everything in the world is connected, and everything is governed by unchangeable laws'.[4] This 'science of order' was on show at the new Royal Museum of Physics and Natural History.

In his foundation of the public museum, Pietro Leopoldo called on his court scientist, the redoubtable natural

FIGURE 5
Detail of an 'anatomical Venus', made around 1800, at La Specola, Florence. Photograph by Tanya Marcuse, *Wax Bodies*, N°71, 2006.

FIGURE 6
Wax models in glass cases, made around 1800, at La Specola, Florence. Photograph by Tanya Marcuse, *Wax Bodies*, N°42, 2006.

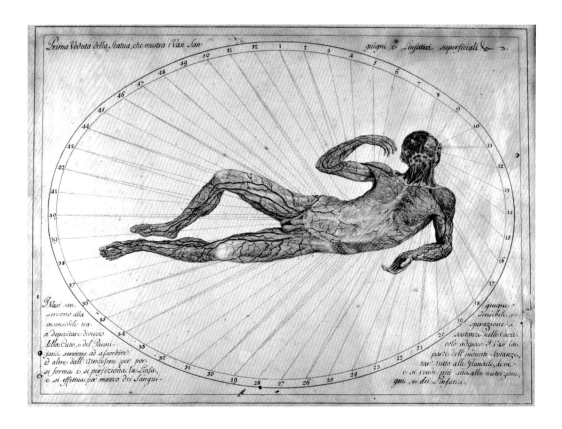

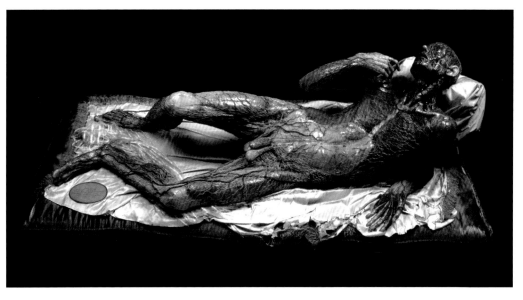

FIGURE 7 (OPPOSITE, TOP)
Drawing of 'the flayed man', made
around 1800, at La Specola, Florence.
Photograph by Saulo Bambi.

FIGURE 8 (OPPOSITE, BOTTOM)
Il scorticato ('the flayed man')
in wax, made around 1800,
at La Specola, Florence.
Photograph by Saulo Bambi.

FIGURE 9 (ABOVE)
The Grand Duke's chemistry
cabinet, 18th century.
Photograph by Museo Galileo,
Institute and Museum of the
History of Science, Florence.

philosopher Felice Fontana (1730–1805, Figure 10), who became the museum's first director. Fontana supported the Grand Duke's political course of public enlightenment; he confidently proclaimed that the museum would 'enlighten the public and make it happy by making it civilised'.[5] But setting up a public museum for the purposes of enlightenment and improvement opened up a number of practical questions: what objects should be put on display to produce public enlightenment? How should the encounter between models and visitors be shaped to achieve the collection's 'civilising mission'?

The Grand Duke and his scientist employed a range of measures to obtain objects for the museum. They selected pieces from the old cabinet of curiosities of the now-defunct Medici dynasty; they called for donations from citizens, and in the early 1770s Fontana and his assistant Giovanni Fabbroni travelled to

France and England to purchase instruments and specimens. Transfers from the cabinet of curiosities, in particular, posed the question of whether an object was more appropriate for the new art gallery, the Uffizi, or for the science museum. A series of miniature scenes of death and decay produced by Gaetano Zumbo in the seventeenth century, for instance, was considered too morbid and gaudy for the Uffizi but not sufficiently anatomical for La Specola (Figure 11).

The best way to ensure that objects were appropriate for the museum's civilising mission was to make them in-house. Thus, Fontana created two workshops within the museum itself, one for the production of scientific instruments, and one for anatomical models. Fontana was obsessed with the perfection of the artificial anatomies. Given the privilege of using bodies from the General Hospital and the orphanage, he regularly received body parts (between 100–200 per year), delivered by Giacinto Guidetti, the unfortunate dogsbody of the museum. Guidetti complained bitterly that 'in times of rain or snow [...] he cannot take a break anywhere, since he carries with him the basket with dead bodies, which task makes him detestable to everyone, and he is treated badly in the coffee houses, which he used to frequent'.[6] He also received some abuse from physicians and surgeons at the General Hospital who used corpses (that were unclaimed by relatives) for teaching and resented the museum's competition for the precious resource. They rejected Fontana's claim that models could replace corpses in medical education.

Models were produced in collaboration between artisans and anatomists. A dissector prepared specimens in poses adopted from established anatomical textbooks such as those of Andreas Vesalius, Bernhard Siegfried Albinus (see Hendriksen, Huistra and Knoeff in this volume), and Samuel Thomas Sömmering. Preparations were then imitated by the modellers in wax, and medically trained museum visitors recognised these poses approvingly. The serene, authoritative wax models on display do not reveal the tensions and conflicts 'behind the

FIGURE 10
Felice Fontana (1730–1805), first director of the Royal Museum of Physics and Natural History, La Specola. Photograph by Museo Galileo, Institute and Museum of the History of Science, Florence.

scenes' between modellers and scientists. Director Fontana considered himself the true author of the anatomical models, since he had developed the method of presentation and possessed anatomical knowledge. He claimed that his relationship with the modellers was straightforwardly instrumental and hierarchical, and that he used the modellers as he would use mere 'tools'.[7] The modellers, however, resisted such instrumentalisation and submission, and insisted on a degree of autonomy. Their craft knowledge of materials and techniques was unique and could not easily be replaced or controlled. Thus modeller Niccolò Cappeletti, for instance, stole wax from the museum to supply his own business of making portrait busts, and boasted that 'regarding the wax, none of those simpletons at the museum can find him out as turpentine hides everything'. Mixing wax with turpentine to change its properties and proportions, he thwarted administrators' efforts to keep track of quantities of materials.[8]

Such conflicts were invisible to the many visitors who came to see the Royal Museum. The new institution was explicitly open to anyone, free of charge, although Fontana advised the porters not to admit 'unsuitable [...] persons, and only a few peasants, but not too many'.[9] Visitors came from all ranks of society. The Grand Duke's own children were taught there by their tutors. But more humble Florentines also made their way to the museum, as did French, German, and British travellers on the Grand Tour, and a range of professionals, from doctors to clergymen. Families brought their children and visitor numbers grew to an average of 100 per day.

The exhibition gave equal weight to all parts of the creation, presenting minerals, plants, animals, and human bodies in showcases of similar design. However, audiences clearly responded to one part of the collection in particular: the anatomical models. The models were singled out in travellers' accounts as the most spectacular aspect of the Florentine museum and the floor had to be repaired more frequently in the anatomical section than elsewhere in the showrooms.

FIGURE 11
The Triumph of Time, Gaetano Zumbo,
1690s, at La Specola, Florence.
Photograph by Saulo Bambi.

Audiences understood the anatomical model collection in their own ways, which did not always coincide with the intentions of the sovereign and his scientist – an experience familiar to museum practitioners to the present day. Fontana must have been gratified to read the accounts published around 1800 by the German physician Engelbert Wichelhausen and by the French surgeon René-Nicolas Desgenettes – both affirmed that the anatomical waxes represented 'the most interesting new discoveries'. They praised the models for their 'elegance, precision and truth', the Grand Duke for his 'true sovereign grandeur', and Fontana himself for his 'deep natural knowledge, plentiful artistry, iron patience, and felicitous genius'.[10] Other visitors, however, failed to confirm the Grand Duke's and the museum director's shared vision of enlightenment and rationality through anatomical education. French magistrate Charles Dupaty praised the models as occasions for moral contemplation: 'philosophy has been wrong, in not examining still deeper the physical parts of man; it is there the moral man is hidden.' Painter Elisabeth Vigée-Lebrun responded to the models with deep religious sentiment: 'it is not possible to contemplate the structure of the human body without feeling convinced of some divine power [...] in M. Fontana's laboratory one kneels and believes'.[11] We know little of the responses of less literate visitors who did not leave written accounts of their experience but it may be indicative that the administrators soon decided to put locks on the showcases displaying the genitals.

Visitors responded to the models in idiosyncratic ways that did not necessarily fit the sovereign's and Fontana's vision of public enlightenment. Experts at the museum responded to this problem in different ways: Fontana claimed that enabling physical interaction would make models more useful, and in the late 1780s he began to experiment with wood as an alternative to the fragile wax to create 'dissectible' models. By contrast, his second-in-command Giovanni Fabbroni proposed that teachers should be present to shape and control the encounter between visitors and models.

However, the problem of multiple interpretations, which so vexed Fontana, came to be useful for ensuring the continuing existence of the museum beyond Pietro Leopoldo's experiment in public enlightenment. In the nineteenth and twentieth centuries, collection managers used the flexible meanings of the models to develop new arguments for the preservation of the collection, adapting their uses to changing social and political contexts. These included new initiatives to promote higher education during the years of Tuscany's inclusion in the French empire after the Napoleonic occupation, and the collection's return to the status of private cabinet of curiosities with the restoration of Pietro Leopoldo's son Francis to the Grand Duchy.

Today, La Specola serves as the zoological museum of the University of Florence, and plays host to a range of activities. Lively school groups explore the displays of stuffed animals, while backstage at the museum researchers investigate subjects ranging from bats to beetles. The anatomical waxes have recently been the basis for a collaborative project between the museum and the university's medical faculty, using images of the models on CD as a means of teaching anatomy to medical students. Beyond this recent return to anatomical education, the models continue to fascinate visitors who have escaped the crowds at Florentine churches and art galleries, and they continue to inspire artists' reflections on death and beauty.

NOTES

Figures 3, 5 and 6: see www.tanyamarcuse.com.

1. Thomas Schnalke, 'Der expandierende Mensch – Zur Konstitution von Körperbildern in anatomischen Sammlungen des 18. Jahrhunderts', in *Medizin, Geschichte und Geschlecht: Körperhistorische Rekonstruktionen von Identitäten und Differenzen*, ed. by Frank Stahnisch and Florian Steger (Stuttgart: Franz Steiner, 2005), pp. 63–82.

2. For a larger selection of images from La Specola see also *Museo zoologico La Specola, Encyclopaedia Anatomica* (Cologne: Taschen, 1999).

3. Quoted in Charles Dupaty, *Sentimental Letters on Italy* (London: Crowder and Bew, 1789), pp. 99–100.

4. *Novelle letterarie* no.1 (1777); quoted in Anna Maerker, *Model Experts: Wax Anatomies and Enlightenment in Florence and Vienna, 1775–1815* (Manchester: Manchester University Press, 2011), pp. 27–8.

5. *Saggio del Real Gabinetto di Fisica, e di Storia Naturale di Firenze* (Rome: Giovanni Zempel, 1775), p. 4.

6. Maerker, *Model Experts*, p. 88.

7. Renato G Mazzolini, 'Plastic Anatomies and Artificial Dissections', in *Models: The Third Dimension of Science*, ed. by Sorayah de Chadarevian and Nick Hopwood (Stanford: Stanford University Press, 2004), pp. 43–70.

8. Museo Galileo, Florence, archives of the Royal Museum of Physics and Natural History, Filza di negozi dell'anno 1789B, fol. 482v.

9. Museo Galileo, Florence, archives of the Royal Museum of Physics and Natural History, Filza di negozi dell'anno 1789A, fol. 278v, 279.

10. Engelbert Wichelhausen, *Ideen über die beste Anwendung der Wachsbildnerei* (Frankfurt am Main: JLE Zessler, 1798), pp. 36, 95; René Desgenettes, 'Réflexions générales sur l'utilité de l'anatomie artificielle', *Observations sur la physique, sur l'histoire naturelle et sur les arts*, 43 (1793), pp. 81–94 (p. 93).

11. Dupaty, *Sentimental Letters*, p. 128; *The Memoirs of Elisabeth Vigée-Lebrun*, trans. Siân Evans (Bloomington: Indiana University Press, 1996), p. 123.

Making space for specimens

The museums of the Karolinska Institute, Stockholm

Eva Åhrén

In the late summer of 1854, Anders Retzius, professor of anatomy and Inspector of the Karolinska Institute in Stockholm, received a curious delivery from Dr Engelbrecht in Söderköping, a provincial town in southern Sweden. The package contained a pickled specimen in a glass jar accompanied by a letter explaining the contents. Cholera had hit Söderköping that summer and Engelbrecht had made a startling find among the bodies he autopsied: a hermaphrodite. The body had fully developed breasts but genitalia that appeared to be somewhere in between male and female. Excited about his finding, Engelbrecht wrote up the case history of seventy-five-year-old Bertha Dittlöf, preserved her extraordinary pelvis, and shipped it intact to Retzius.

This chapter traces the history of the Karolinska Institute's collections through the nineteenth century when Stockholm was emerging as a well-connected scientific centre linked to international knowledge communities and networks of exchange. It discusses the fate of the medical museum as a site for education and research in the context of changing scientific ideals and practices. Though today little remains of the institute's once extensive collections, nevertheless they form a valuable if currently underused medical and cultural heritage (Figure 1).

FIGURE 1 (OPPOSITE)
Gallery view of the Karolinska Institute's anatomy museum around 1930, before the institute moved to new premises and disbanded the museums of the old campus in central Stockholm. Courtesy of The Hagströmer Medico-Historical Library.

FROM ECLECTIC TO SYSTEMATIC

The Karolinska Institute opened in 1810 as a school for surgeons. At first, the school's museum was an eclectic one-room display of objects relating to natural history, anatomy, pathology, pharmacology and surgery. However, under the leadership of world-renowned chemist Jöns Jacob Berzelius, the faculty started transforming the institute into a prominent medical school and scientific research centre. To achieve this, they needed to set up systematic collections of specimens: the foundational medical science of the time was anatomy, and anatomical research depended on large collections for comparative analysis.[1]

The museum started expanding in the mid-1820s, after Berzelius hired Anders Retzius as professor and curator. Retzius studied anatomy collections on trips abroad and brought back new knowledge and ideas, which he then implemented in the museum. When Retzius visited Breslau, Prussia (now Wrocław, Poland), in 1833, anatomist Jan Purkyně introduced him to a

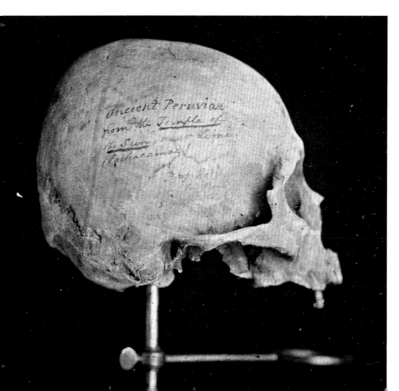

FIGURE 2
Photograph by anatomist Gustaf Retzius (son of Anders Retzius) of a human cranium from Peru, held at the Karolinska Institute's anatomy museum. This was donated by anatomist and physician Samuel Morton, based in Philadelphia, in exchange for skulls of Finnish, Sami, and Eastern European origin. The photograph was taken for Anders Retzius's collected writings on craniology, *Ethnologische Schriften: Nach dem Tode des Verfassers gesammelt*, ed. Gustaf Retzius (Stockholm, 1864).
Courtesy of the Center for History of Science, Royal Swedish Academy of Sciences.

pedagogical programme based on observation and experience, inspired by Swiss educational reformer Johann Heinrich Pestalozzi. Impressed, Retzius fashioned his own museum into a sophisticated teaching aid. Retzius and his colleagues used specimens as instructional tools (alongside visual and textual media such as charts, blackboards, drawings, books, and prints) to complement lectures and hands-on dissections. Professors prepared their own specimens to demonstrate in the classroom, and students used the collections for self-instruction.

Although there was no fixed boundary between specimens intended for research and those intended for teaching, some were made specifically for the latter and were kept in a storage room next to the lecture hall. That said, the museum was first and foremost a scientific resource: anatomists created specimens in the course of pursuing their studies. These specimens were the tangible proof of new research findings and could also contribute to further studies, as when Retzius pulled teeth from skeletons in the museum for his celebrated study of comparative dental histology.[2] The museum was not only an archive of research undertaken but also a repository of future research material.

Specimens came from many sources. Cadavers for anatomical dissection were received from clinics affiliated with the institute; this practice was regulated by law and Swedish medical schools never experienced grave-robbing scandals like those in Britain and the US.[3] Pathological specimens were sent to the professors at the Karolinska Institute from physicians in Stockholm and elsewhere. There was considerable prestige to be gained from having one's name associated with an important specimen and with the publications of leading scientists at the institute. Animal specimens of many kinds were also sent to the institute from Sweden and all over the world. Retzius, for example, made good use of a python from Bengal, which he received from his friend Sven Nilsson, a renowned naturalist. The python became an object of study in comparative anatomy; a parasitic worm from its intestines had a study of its own and one

FIGURE 3
Preserved specimens used to teach comparative anatomy and embryology with reference to the foetal development of the domestic cat (around 1900). The bottom two specimens have colored wax injected into the uterine blood vessels.
Photograph by Ulf Sirborn.

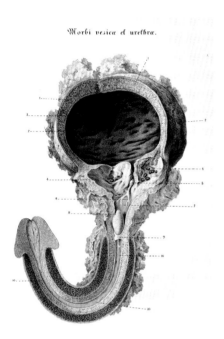

Morbi vesicæ et urethræ.

FIGURE 4
Lithograph by A Hårdh depicting a
penis with a urethral stricture that
had caused complications (including
a urinary calculus) in an adult male,
from *Museum anatomicum Holmiense
quod auspiciis augustissimi Regis
Oscaris I eviderunt*, ed. Anders
Retzius (Holmiae, 1855). This
book was planned as the first in a
series on pathological specimens
at the Karolinska Institute's
anatomy museum but subsequent
volumes were not published.
Courtesy of Uppsala University Library.

of its teeth formed part of Retzius's dental studies.[4] Scientists exchanged specimens with other members of their professional networks. Models and specimens were bought from traders in and outside of Sweden and explorers and expatriates donated or sold skulls, plants, and animal skeletons to the institute (Figures 2 and 3).

The character of the collections changed in conjunction with changing scientific and educational principles, trends, and demands. Retzius introduced and established comparative, topographical and pathological anatomy as well as histology, morphology, and craniology as topics of research and education at the institute (Figure 4). The specimens and models he produced and acquired reflect his scientific interests, organised in a systematic way. In the 1850s the museum filled nine rooms in the institute's main building, one of which was a grand hall with a gallery where large animal skeletons were displayed, including an African elephant, a giraffe, an aurochs, an ostrich, and a walrus.

THE UNIQUE AND THE SERIES

Retzius was delighted to receive the unusual genitalia of Bertha Dittlöf in the late summer of 1854. He dissected and analysed them, published the study in the medical journal *Hygiea*, and circulated it as an offprint of four pages plus two plates with etchings.[5] He also gave a talk on the case at a meeting with the Swedish Society of Medicine. Finally, Retzius added the specimen to the extensive collections and the catalogue of the anatomy museum at the Karolinska Institute, where it served as material proof of his scientific paper. It was displayed in one of the many cabinets and could be taken out for demonstrations to medical students and other visitors – the museum was open to the public by appointment but it was primarily a professional collection, made by and for physicians, scientists, and students of medicine and surgery.

Retzius, however, did not believe in the concept of hermaphroditism – he was convinced that human bodies were either male or female depending on whether they had testicles or ovaries, even if the secondary sexual characteristics were ambiguous. After studying the external and internal genitalia he concluded that Dittlöf's body was, in fact, male, since it lacked a vagina and had testicles and a prostate – although these were underdeveloped and misplaced. He used the specimen and the case history to illustrate and argue for a theory of foetal development, which he had adopted in the 1820s and later refined through his own and other anatomists' work. The theory held that sexual development in the foetus could go wrong and cause incompletely formed sex organs. This theory was supported by Retzius's good friend, renowned German anatomist Johannes Müller.[6] In the same article Retzius also referred to a series of embryos that he had dissected and prepared for his anatomy museum at the institute, which illustrated foetal genital development and malformations (Figure 5).

Dittlöf kept her ambiguous genitals a secret during her lifetime. Her body became an object of scientific study after her death and her genitals were transformed into a museum specimen showcasing developmental anomalies; the unique specimen became just one part of an extended series. Yet in his article about this 'case of hypospadias' and 'mistaken gender,' Retzius devoted some space to Dittlöf's life, thereby preserving aspects of her individuality.[7] His writing thus provides a glimpse of one of the many individuals who unwittingly, and sometimes unwillingly, gave up parts of their bodies to museum science.

SPECIALISING AND PROLIFERATING

Other scientists continued to add to the collections after Retzius's death in 1860. While Retzius had lectured in a variety of overlapping areas (both normal and morbid anatomy, physiology, histology, embryology, zoology, forensic medicine and more), his colleagues and successors established these as separate

FIGURE 5
Illustrations of the development of genital malformations in the human foetus, based on specimens in the Karolinska Institute's anatomy museum. Anders Retzius, 'Händelse af hypospadi', *Hygiea*, 1854.
Courtesy of the National Library of Medicine.

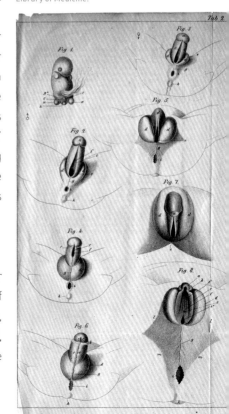

disciplines during the latter half of the nineteenth century. A museum space with specimens on display was essential in building and professionalising a scientific institution, as were other indicators of status such as a professorial chair, a published journal, a textbook and regular meetings. This resulted in a second phase of expansion for the museum collections at the Karolinska Institute during the latter part of the nineteenth century: a number of departmental museums were created, breaking out from the anatomy museum.

When the department of pathological anatomy opened in 1866 it included the first of these specialised museums (others followed, including forensic medicine, hygiene, obstetrics and gynaecology, dermatology and venereal disease, and psychiatry). This museum comprised three halls, one of which was an expansive 130m^2 with a gallery. It formed the centre of the department, surrounded by other necessary spaces: cold storage for cadavers in the basement, laboratories, dissection halls for humans and animals, stables, lecture halls equipped with microscopes and blackboards, and a photographic studio in the attic (Figure 6). The building was fitted with the latest innovations such as hydraulic elevators, running hot water, central heating and a sewer system that flushed detritus straight into the adjacent lake. Everything was planned by Axel Key, professor of pathology, who had made notes on the best features of pathology departments around Europe – most notably Rudolph Virchow's institute in Berlin, where he had spent a year studying (see Schnalke in this volume).[8]

The Karolinska Institute's museums contained more than just dried bones and preserved organs of humans and animals: there were also models. The most precious ones – a full-scale model of a female body and several body parts – were donated in 1825 by Crown Prince Oscar of Sweden, who commissioned them from the famous workshop at 'La Specola' in Florence (see Maerker in this volume) (Figures 7 and 8). Other models were

FIGURE 6
Photograph of a skeleton posed outside a building (presumably to get as much light as possible to aid the photographic process) from the early days of photography at the Karolinska Institute, around 1860. The wet plate collodion process used here was notoriously difficult and in this case the resulting print resembles a negative. Image courtesy of the Center for History of Science, Royal Swedish Academy of Sciences.

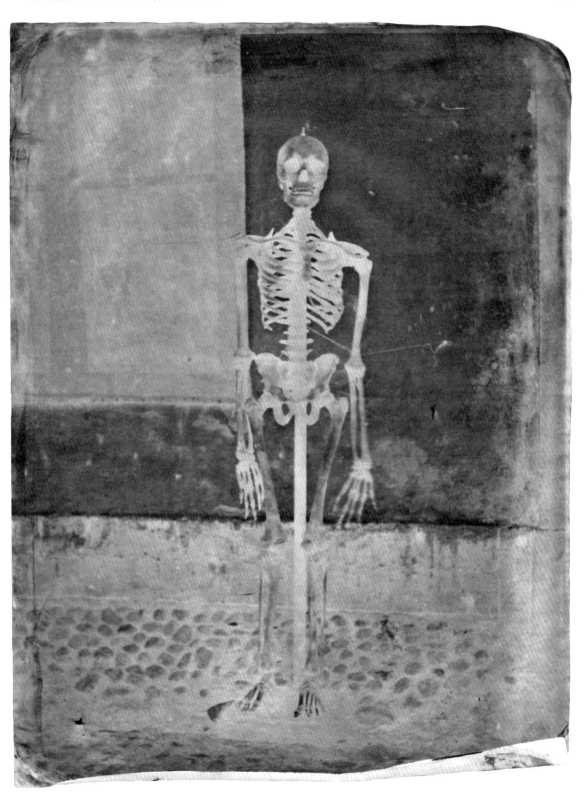

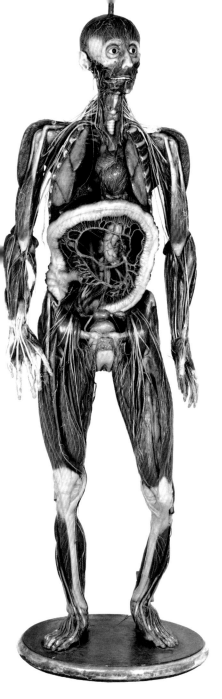

more prosaic: plaster casts that were sturdy enough to be passed around students in the classrooms. Embryological models gave shape to minuscule structures and helped both scientists and students make sense of foetal development (Figure 9).[9] A collection of extremely realistic wax casts, moulages, became important as a three-dimensional reference atlas for venereal and skin diseases – a standing it kept well into the twentieth century (Figure 10). The collections kept on growing, so much so that in 1910 pathology professor Carl Sundberg complained that he spent much of his time 'making space for specimens.'[10]

The third expansion of the Karolinska Institute's specimen collections happened in the late nineteenth century, when the rising importance of microscopic studies across the disciplines resulted in a growing number of glass slides. Tissue samples were stained, fixed, embedded in paraffin, sliced with the help of microtomes, and mounted on glass. These specimens did not need to be displayed on museum shelves: any department could assemble thousands of slides in one cabinet, so even if the number of specimens grew enormously they still only needed a tiny amount of space compared with gross anatomy specimens (Figures 11 and 12). Medical cases were also increasingly documented by means of photography and photomicrography, making the laborious collection and maintenance of displays of larger pathological specimens less attractive.

INTO STORAGE

Dittlöf's genitalia were unique, and the specimen was a valuable addition to the collection of anomalies in the anatomy museum of the Karolinska Institute. It can also serve as an example of the complex historical roles of specimens in anatomy museums. First, what originated as a body part of an individual became an object used to showcase a particular physical structure. Second, it was acquired through a professional network, which was in turn strengthened by the exchange. Third, the major interest for the scientists was not in the object as a

FIGURE 7
Life-size wax model of female anatomy from the workshop of Francesco Calenzoli at La Specola in Florence. It was donated to the Karolinska institute by Crown Prince Oscar of Sweden in 1825. Photograph by Ulf Sirborn.

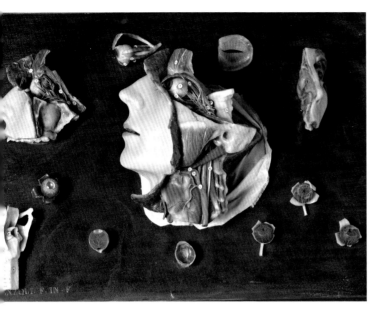

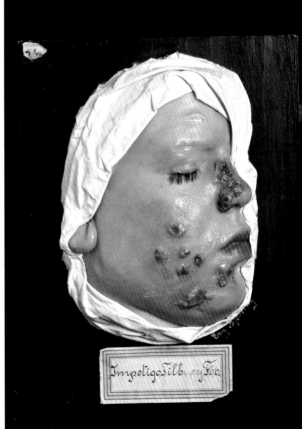

FIGURE 8 (LEFT)
Wax anatomical models of the human eye. They were produced at Francesco Calenzoli's workshop at 'La Specola' in Florence and donated to the Karolinska Institute by Crown Prince Oscar of Swden in 1825.
Photograph by Ulf Sirborn.

FIGURE 9 (BELOW, LEFT)
Wax model of the head of a human foetus at nine weeks of gestation, focusing on the development of the face, around 1911. They were produced at Friedrich Ziegler's firm, in Freiburg, in collaboration with Dr Karl Peter in Greifswald.
Photograph by Ulf Sirborn.

FIGURE 10 (BELOW, RIGHT)
Moulage of a boy with impetigo, an infectious skin disease, around 1900. Artist unknown.
Photograph by Ulf Sirborn.

curiosity but rather in the knowledge that could be gained from
it in light of what was already known, and in comparison with
specimens already collected. Fourth, the specimen was used
in scientific communication and education using diverse media:
the written case history, catalogue entry and scientific articles;
spoken lectures to peers and students; demonstrations and
displays of the actual specimen; drawings, etchings and prints
representing it and the knowledge gained from it.[11] Fifth, it was
used to strengthen and illustrate a particular scientific theory
as part of a larger series of specimens. Finally, it contributed to
building personal, institutional, and national prestige. Medical
museums were places for receptions and meetings – spaces that
displayed not only specimens but also institutional stature. The

specimens thus had much rhetorical value beyond the scientific and educational.

Medical museums have since changed character because of changing practices and ideals in medical science and education over the past century and a half. Many gross anatomical specimens were abandoned for microscopic slides; drawings, prints and photographs often became more important than the specimens themselves. With the rising status of experimental science, the laboratory rivalled the museum as a key locus of scientific work. In the mid-twentieth century many museums lost their standing as primary places for medical training and research, and some became dusty displays of outdated science in an age obsessed with progress and modernity.

For the Karolinska Institute's museums, the most dramatic change happened when the institute moved to a new campus in a Stockholm suburb in the 1940s. The plans for the new campus allowed no space for museum displays or extensive collections. A few specimens were kept in cabinets in various departments but many others were put away in storage or discarded. Over the years, the number of preserved specimens has further diminished. Selected objects from the Karolinska Institute were put on display at the Museum of Medical History on the institute's

FIGURE 12
Cabinet containing microscope slides of preserved brains from various animal species, around 1900. From left to right, there are slices of the brains of a horse, an iguana and a domestic cat. To the far right are brain slices of the Atlantic hagfish; a species of particular interest to evolutionary biologists, which were prepared by Anders Retzius while collaborating with Johannes Müller at the west coast of Sweden.
Photograph by Ulf Sirborn.

FIGURE 13
Uncatalogued preparation of the
human head and neck, most probably
used to teach topographical anatomy,
1850–1900. It is currently shelved
with other skulls, specimens in
jars, hospital furniture, 19th-
century physiotherapy equipment,
x-ray machinery, and discarded
exhibition material. These objects
were salvaged from the Karolinska
Institute's museum collections by
the Friends of the Museum of the
History of Medicine in Stockholm.
Funding for the museum has
run out and the collection is
now stored in a warehouse.
Photograph by Ulf Sirborn

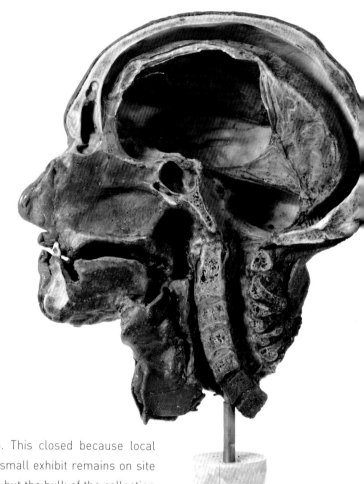

campus between 1995 and 2005. This closed because local
government funding dried up – a small exhibit remains on site
and can be viewed by appointment but the bulk of the collection
remains inaccessible in a remote storage facility south of
Stockholm. The Society of Friends of the Museum of Medical
History is struggling to preserve this medical heritage but the
future is insecure, especially during this time of financial crises
and shrinking budgets for social welfare and cultural heritage
(Figure 13).[12]

ACKNOWLEDGEMENTS

Research for this chapter was made possible by a
generous grant from Riksbankens Jubileumsfond.

NOTES

1. See John Pickstone, *Ways of Knowing: A New History of Science, Technology and Medicine* (Chicago: University of Chicago Press, 2001).

2. Anders Retzius, 'Mikroskopiska undersökningar öfver Tändernes, särdeles Tandbenets, struktur', Kongl. *Vetenskaps-academiens handlingar, för år 1836* (Stockholm: Norstedts, 1837), pp. 52–140.

3. Eva Åhrén, *Death, Modernity, and the Body: Sweden 1870–1940* (Rochester: University of Rochester press, 2009); Helen MacDonald, *Human Remains: Dissection and its Histories* (New Haven: Yale University Press, 2005); Ruth Richardson, *Death, Dissection and the Destitute* (London: Routledge and Kegan Paul, 1988); Michael Sappol, *A Traffic of Dead Bodies: Anatomy and Embodied Social Identity in Nineteenth-Century America* (Princeton: Princeton University Press, 2002).

4. Anders Retzius, 'Anatomisk undersökning öfver några delar af Python bivittatus jemte komparativa anmärkningar', Kongl. *Vetenskaps-academiens handlingar, för år 1830* (Stockholm: Norstedts, 1831), pp. 81–116; 'Beskrivning öfver en ny art af spolmask, funnen hos Python bivittatus, jemte anatomiska anmärkningar', Kongl. *Vetenskaps-academiens handlingar, för år 1829* (Stockholm: Norstedts, 1830), pp. 103–8.

5. Anders Retzius, 'Händelse af hypospadi, som gifvit anledning till misstag om kön, iakttagen af Hr. Stadsläkaren Dr CW Engelbrecht i Söderköping och beskrifven, jemte tillägg om de yttre genitaliernas utvecklingsformer', *Hygiea: Medicinsk och Pharmaceutisk Månadsskrift*, 16 (1854), pp. 544–49. See also Maja Bondestam, *Tvåkönad: Den svenska hermafroditens historia* (Nora: Nya Doxa, 2010); Alice Domurat Dreger, *Hermaphrodites and the Medical Invention of Sex* (Cambridge, Mass.: Harvard University Press, 1998); Elizabeth Reis, *Bodies in Doubt: An American History of Intersex* (Baltimore: Johns Hopkins University Press, 2009).

6. Johannes Müller, *Bildungsgeschichte der Genitalien aus anatomische Untersuchungen an Embryonen des Menschen und der Thiere: Nebst einem Anhang über die chirurgische Behandlung der Hypospadia* (Düsseldorf: Arnz, 1830).

7. Retzius, 'Händelse af hypospadi', p. 544.

8. Axel Key, 'Om den nya Patologiskt Anatomiska Institutionen i Stockholm', *Nordiskt Medicinskt Arkiv*, 1 (1869), pp. 1–27.

9. See Nick Hopwood, *Embryos in Wax: Models from the Ziegler Studio* (Cambridge: Whipple Museum, University of Cambridge, 2002).

10. Carl Sundberg, 'Patologisk-anatomska institutionen', *Karolinska mediko-kirurgiska institutets historia, bd III*, eds. JG Edgren, F Lennmalm, & S Jolin (Stockholm: Isaac Marcus Boktryckeri, 1910), pp. 347–411.

11. See Elizabeth Hallam, *Anatomy Museum. Death and the Body Displayed* (London: Reaktion Books, forthcoming 2014).

12. http://medicinhistoriskastockholm.se/gamla_sidan/projekt.swf.

FIGURE 1
Displays in storage rooms
organised by GA Wehrli, 1934.
Institute and Museum of the
History of Medicine Zurich.

The Museum of the History of Medicine in Zurich

Flurin Condrau

The Institute and Museum of the History of Medicine of the University of Zurich is home to one of the largest collections of medical artefacts, manuscripts and books in the world.[1] Its potential is huge: there is a substantial specialist library, a large collection of objects, and an archive of personal papers and institutional records. The museum, with 400m^2 of space, houses a permanent exhibition that opened in 1990 as well as changing special exhibitions. There has been some recent development of parts of the collections, yet there are substantial tasks ahead to make sure that best practice in collections management is followed and that the museum is integrated into research and teaching. This chapter briefly discusses the history of the institute's museum and collections, and considers their current situation before sketching a possible future for them.

FROM 'MESS' TO MUSEUM

Gustav Adolf Wehrli, a local medical doctor in Zurich, began to collect medical artefacts (based on his interests in local anthropology) around 1915.[2] This collection was stored in the university's main building from 1920, where it remained until the late 1990s. When Wehrli became a lecturer in the history of medicine he planned a Swiss Museum of the History of

Medicine, or a Swiss Museum of Hygiene, but these were never built. Wehrli continued to work with and grow the collection but, housed as it was in substandard accommodation, he did not seek to attract much public interest in it.[3] The bulk of the collection assembled by Wehrli came from departments of the university hospital; artefacts relating to non-Western medicine were also collected, several of which arrived in Zurich during the 1920s from the Museum of Anthropology in Hamburg. Wehrli was an active member of the Swiss Society for Local Anthropology, which may explain his interest in these objects (Figures 1 and 2).

Following Wehrli's death in 1949, there was a brief interlude under the guidance of Bernhard Milt, the first professor of history of medicine at the University of Zurich. Success arrived with the appointment of Erwin H Ackerknecht, who served as the director of the Institute of the History of Medicine from 1957 to 1971. He brought previous experience of museum work (at the American Museum of Natural History in New York) as well as authority in the history of medicine; he was considered one of the leading figures in this emerging academic field.

Ackerknecht's arrival in Zurich is well documented through letters and reports. In conversations he recalled the chaos he encountered in the collections. In a letter to his friend and mentor Henry Sigerist, at Johns Hopkins University in Baltimore, he declared the institute 'a mess'.[4] His first annual report complained that Wehrli had left large parts of the collection uncatalogued and disorganised. He announced that the collection needed a firm hand to restore order, and identified many so-called duplicate objects (ones that closely resembled others) to be removed and shifted elsewhere. Ackerknecht convinced the university to invest in a refurbishment of the old tower housing the collection. Here was launched the first permanent exhibition of the history of medicine at this institution for the general public on 6 November 1961 (Figure 3). Witnessing this event were Zurich's minister of education, the chancellor of the university, and the dean of the medical school. Visitors were

FIGURE 2
Displays in storage rooms
organised by GA Wehrli, undated.
Institute and Museum of the
History of Medicine Zurich.

apparently invited to view display cabinets illustrating medicine during historical periods such as the Middle Ages, medical specialties such as ophthalmology and dentistry, and practices such as medical diagnosis and therapy.[5]

Ackerknecht's vision for a museum of the history of medicine is difficult to reconstruct but an indication of it is provided in a publication from 1963. Here he argued that, alongside the written word, objects needed to be taken seriously as sources for the history of medicine. Indeed, objects had 'greater emotional impact', he claimed, and offered more 'direct' access to the past than words.[6] By Ackerknecht's own high standards, though, the call to use objects as historical sources perhaps remained more a commitment to education rather than a fundamental shift in the way historians worked with collections in their research (Figure 4).

The next professor and director of the institute, Huldrych M Koelbing (in post 1971 to 1988) refurbished the museum for opening in 1972 – again, local dignitaries were present. Koelbing left Ackerknecht's museum arrangement largely intact, rather than presenting new themes, objects or ideas.[7] In 1978 the museum's first full-time curator was appointed, who then concentrated on maintaining the collection and producing a new catalogue to replace Wehrli's old system. But Koelbing was unable to sustain the reputation that the institute held under Ackerknecht. He remained convinced, however, that the history of medicine as a university subject would best survive on the basis of a museum. He secured the appointment of a new museum curator in 1985 and oversaw the move of the museum to new premises as well as the plans for the permanent exhibition that launched in 1990.

Koelbing's successor as director, Beat Rüttimann (in post 1990 to 2010) – a Swiss orthopaedic surgeon with interests in the history of medicine – guided the museum to premises at Raemistrasse 69, which is its present location. With this relocation the public galleries were separated from the rooms

FIGURE 3
Museum display cabinets organised by EH Ackerknecht and M Curti, 1961. Institute and Museum of the History of Medicine Zurich.

that store the museum's collections, and so the museum was situated at a distance both from its collections and also from academic research. Since then the museum has not been regularly used in teaching and research and its exhibition has largely remained unchanged despite scholarly critique.[8]

PROBLEMS AND POTENTIAL

However, the museum's accommodation at Raemistrasse 69, one of the oldest university buildings on the central campus, now offers fantastic potential for developing exhibitions, teaching and research with the collections. It includes, for instance, Albert Einstein's office, which he occupied as a lecturer in physics around 1909. Much more could be done by way of displays that explore his work, beyond the commemorative plaque displayed in the relevant room. Physiology was taught in the building until 1983, and generations of Swiss doctors still remember lectures in the vicinity of the museum. WR Hess, winner of the Nobel Prize in Physiology, 1949, worked in this building too (Figure 5). Plans for the museum could draw upon these local memories to explore how knowledge has been made and communicated in this very building. Furthermore, exhibitions require critical re-thinking. Currently they tend to present aspects of the past as problematic in comparison to supposedly advanced modern medicine. The museum therefore conveys a simplified view of past and present medical history, for example in the display of infectious diseases. The museum could examine these issues from different perspectives as well as addressing many others, such as the changing encounters between patients and healers.

Under its present leadership, with strong connections to the international scholarly community in the history of medicine, there have been moves to reshape the museum's identity. The first temporary exhibition held under the new leadership, *Rosenstrumpf und dornencknie*, ran during 2011. The exhibition's title translates as 'rose stocking and thornknee' – the key line of a poem written by a patient in the Rheinau Psychiatric Hospital,

and it featured artworks by patients in this hospital from 1867 to 1930[9] (Figures 6 and 7). The exhibition presented these patients' experiences through their art, rather than focusing on doctors' views, thereby offering different insights instead of highlighting those of dominant professionals. Through the development of the exhibition, staff at the institute interacted with colleagues from psychiatry and the ministry of health, so that the museum started to become a platform for communication. Indeed, a newly developed central aim of the museum is to host ongoing, interdisciplinary conversations about medicine and society.

A further special exhibition of 2011 was bought in from the Berlin Museum of Medical History at the Charité Hospital (see Schnalke in this volume). Entitled *Who Cares? History and Everyday Life of Nursing in Germany*, the original exhibition in Berlin was scaled down to fit the museum's temporary exhibition room while retaining its core concerns (Figure 8).[10] Combining present day reflections with historical perspectives, the aim was to communicate with visitors, engage them in dialogue, and stimulate debate about nursing past and present. The exhibition was a platform for further events: a public discussion regarding professional teams in medicine; readings from the diary of Mignon, a Jewish nurse in Nazi-controlled Vienna; and a programme exploring experiences such as 'disgust' using medical films and objects from the collection. The museum is thus being used as a site for reflection, discussion and engagement based on themes that are relevant to academic work as well as being of interest to the public.

Closely associated with the Institute and Museum of the History of Medicine is the Museum of Wax Moulages, located at the University Hospital of Zurich. Housing more than 1,800 models of the body's surface (usually showing skin diseases) from the collections of the Dermatology Clinic and the Clinic of Reconstructive Surgery, this museum has also become a setting for public exhibitions (Figure 9) and university teaching. In the

FIGURE 4 (OPPOSITE, TOP)
EH Ackerknecht in the library, around 1970.
Institute and Museum of the History of Medicine Zurich.

FIGURE 5 (OPPOSITE, BOTTOM)
WR Hess, Nobel Prize winner 1949.
Institute and Museum of the History of Medicine Zurich.

FIGURE 6 (BELOW)
Stocking made of varek (seaweed) and cotton, made by Lisette H (1857–1924) in the Rheinau Psychiatric Hospital.
Sammlung Rheinau, Baudirektion des Kantons Zuerich, Immobilienamt.

FIGURE 7
Embroidery artwork on
cotton, entitled *Ararat*, made
by Johanna (Jeanne) Natalie
Wintsch (1871–1944) in 1924, in
Rheinau Psychiatric Hospital.
Sammlung Rheinau, Baudirektion des
Kantons Zürich, Immobilienamt.

first half of the twentieth century these moulages were moulded from the skin of living hospital patients (Figures 10, 11, 12 and 13).[11] By the 1970s the collection had fallen out of use and was almost forgotten; however, a special exhibition at the Museum of the History of Medicine in 1979, *Wachsbildnerei in der Medizin* (Waxes in Medicine), sparked historical interest in these strikingly realistic models.

Gaining the status of important cultural heritage, around 600 moulages went on public display when the Museum of Wax Moulages opened in 1993 with Elsbeth Stoiber as its first curator. Since 2000, special exhibitions have addressed a range of issues: displaying wax models as documents of historical diseases, exploring the role of moulages as media in public

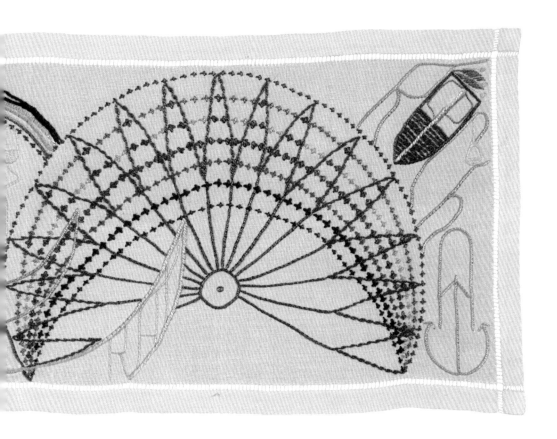

campaigns against sexual diseases (syphilis), and examining the use of moulages in surgical and dermatological research during the 1920s. Michael L Geiges, curator from 1998 and staff physician at the Dermatology Clinic of the University Hospital, has recently revitalised the moulages as dermatology teaching aids, holding lectures in the museum for medical students.[12] To preserve these precious and fragile wax objects, the Museum of Wax Moulages is currently participating in an international conservation project under the direction of the Deutsches Hygiene-Museum in Dresden.[13] At the same time, techniques for making moulages are still practised by the curator and his team, who craft objects for the teaching collection and for dermatology exams.

PURPOSE AND PROSPECT

So how is the future of the Museum of the History of Medicine
to be forged? With an outdated and in some ways problematic
permanent gallery as well as an understaffed, largely
uncatalogued and thus hard-to-use collection of thousands of
objects, the question remains: what is the museum for?

A process of evaluating the museum will be necessary,
which will involve a wide range of local groups with interests
in its development. Finding a new identity for the museum
is very much tied up with creating plans for the future; Samy
Bill, a leading museum consultant in Switzerland, is involved
in this process. As a university museum, emphasis will be on
generating innovative research and encouraging teaching with
the use of the collections. Involvement of the museum's staff in

FIGURE 8 (ABOVE)
Entrance to the *Who Cares?*
exhibition, 2012.
Photograph by Eberhard Wolff,
Institute and Museum of the
History of Medicine Zurich.

FIGURE 9 (OPPOSITE)
Poster for an exhibition in the
Museum of Wax Moulages
in 2002 about the use of wax
moulages in public campaigns
and educational films warning
against syphilis in the 1930s.
Museum of Wax Moulages Zurich.

Feind im Blut

Regie: Walter Ruttmann

Ein Tonfilm vom intimen Leben

Moulagen und Medien im Kampf gegen die Geschlechtskrankheiten

Sonderausstellung
Moulagensammlung Zürich

10. November 2001 bis 29. Mai 2002

Mi 14 – 18 Uhr
Sa 13 – 17 Uhr

Moulagensammlung des UniversitätsSpitals und der Universität Zürich
Haldenbachstrasse 14, 8091 Zürich, Tel. 01 255 56 85, Fax 01 255 44 03
Internet: www.moulagen.ch, E-Mail: geiges@derm.unizh.ch

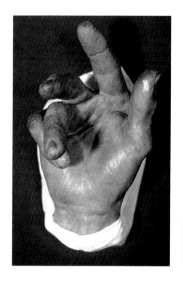
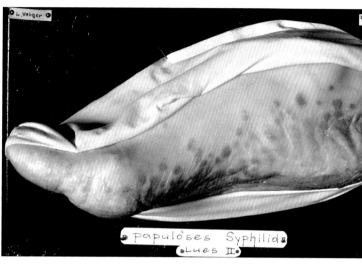

FIGURE 10 (ABOVE, LEFT)
Wax moulage of Dupuytren's
contracture (number 133), made
by Adolf Fleischmann in the Clinic
for Surgery in Zurich in 1920.
Museum of Wax Moulages Zurich.

FIGURE 11 (ABOVE, RIGHT)
Wax moulage of secondary
syphilis (number 487), made by
Lotte Volger in the Dermatology
Clinic in Zurich in 1927.
Museum of Wax Moulages Zurich.

FIGURE 12 (OPPOSITE, TOP)
Wax moulage of *Tinea corporis*
(ringworm) (number 920), made by
Lotte Volger in the Dermatology
Clinic in Zurich in 1940.
Museum of Wax Moulages Zurich.

FIGURE 13 (OPPOSITE, BOTTOM)
Wax moulage of *Psoriasis
gyrata* (number 1275), made by
Ruth Willi in the Dermatology
Clinic in Zurich in 1954.
Museum of Wax Moulages Zurich.

local research networks in Switzerland and elsewhere, such as those working on the history of medicine as well as the history of knowledge and medical ethics, will further link the museum to productive academic environments.

Another key question concerns the relationship between the museum and the contemporary medical environment of the university, which is internationally renowned for its medical research and care. This relationship will be further explored through work in the medical humanities, which in Zurich, as in many universities, is gaining ground within the medical curriculum. The museum may become central to this initiative, providing a forum for interdisciplinary conversations on health, illness and medicine. Bringing the humanities and medicine together may well require a thorough overhaul of the museum and its collections to make exhibitions and material objects inspiring resources for the exploration of medical issues.

ACKNOLWEDGEMENTS

I am grateful to Dr Michael Geiges for the paragraphs on the Museum of Wax Moulages.

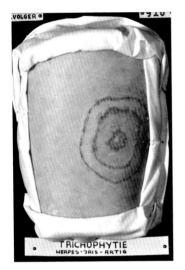

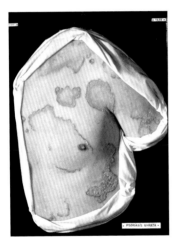

NOTES

1. Urs Boschung, 'Erinnerungen an die alte Medizinhistorische Sammlung', *Gesnerus*, 58 (2001), 220–227.

2. Urs Boschung, 'Gustav Adolf Wehrli' (1888–1949). Gründer der Medizinhistorischen Sammlung der Universität Zürich', *Gesnerus*, 37 (1980), 91–103.

3. Bilderchronik aus dem Turm zu Zürich, Ackerknecht Papers, Institute and Museum of the History of Medicine, University Zurich, Archive MS y 4.

4. *Henry E Sigerist: Correspondences with Welch, Cushing, Garrison, and Ackerknecht* ed. by Marcel Bickel (Bern: Peter Lang, 2010).

5. Medizinhistorisches Museum, Universität Zürich, undated brochure, Institute and Museum of the History of Medicine, Library.

6. Erwin H Ackerknecht, *The World of Asclepios* (Bern: Hans Huber, 1963), p. 5.

7. Urs Boschung, *Medizinhistorische Sammlung der Universität Zürich* (München: Schnell, 1985).

8. Cay-Rüdiger Prüll, 'Medizin im Museum, aber wie? Bemerkungen zur Frage der Museumskonzeption am Beispiel des Medizinhistorischen Museums der Universität Zürich', *Medizin im Museum, Jahrbuch der Medizinhistorischen Sammlung der Ruhr Universität Bochum*, 2 (1995), 19 and 29; Wolfgang U Eckart and Robert Jütte, *Medizingeschichte: Eine Einführung* (Köln: Böhlau, 2007).

9. Katrin Luchsinger, Iris Blum, Jacqueline Fahrni and Monika Jagfeld, *Rosenstrumpf und dornencknie. Werke aus der psychiatrischen Pflegeanstalt Rheinau, 1867–1930* (Zurich: Chronos, 2010).

10. Isabel Atzl, *Who Cares? Geschichte und Alltag der Krankenpflege* (Frankfurt: Mabuse, 2011).

11. Michael L Geiges and Rebekka Holzer, *Dreidimensionale Dokumente – Moulagen zeigen Tierversuche, Selbstversuch und klinische Forschung, Moulagenmuseum der Universität und des Universitätsspitals Zürich* (Zürich: Museum of Wax Moulages Zurich, 2006).

12. Michael L Geiges, 'Wax Moulages in Zurich – Current Relevance for Dermatology, History and the General Public', *Journal für Deutsche Dermatologie Geschichte*, 10 (2007), pp. 953–7.

13. Johanna Lang, Sandra Mühlenberend and Susanne Roessiger, *Körper in Wachs – Moulagen in Forschung und Restaurierung. Sammlungsschwerpunkte. Deutsches Hygiene-Museum*, vol. 3 (Dresden: Sandstein-Verlag, 2010).

Tracing life

The Berlin Museum of Medical History at the Charité

Thomas Schnalke

Visitors walk through 300 years of scientific medicine when they enter the Berlin Museum of Medical History at the Charité Hospital. In doing so, their approach resembles that of the eminent Berlin pathologist Rudolf Virchow (1821–1902) in that he searched for traces of life by looking beneath human skin into organs and bodily structures. After a taste of a 'chamber of wonder' (Figure 1), visitors explore an early eighteenth-century anatomical theatre, reaching the present by way of a private anatomical museum, a pathologist's dissection hall, a medical laboratory and a modern clinical space. Two galleries on the way attract particular attention: the specimen hall presenting a late nineteenth-century arrangement of human diseases, and a historical hospital ward with ten case studies of patients treated in the Charité during its history. The exhibition ends by raising questions for open discussion regarding sensitive issues such as the display of human remains, organ transplantation, genetic research and German medicine under National Socialism.

The museum has been in existence since 1998. The institution aims to showcase medicine in all its complexities, to address not only what medicine is but also how medicine came to be what it is today. In its permanent exhibition, which opened on 25 October 2007, the museum presents the development of medicine

from a Western, natural historical and scientific perspective over the past three centuries.[1] Here the title *Tracing Life* makes a conscious connection to one of modern medicine's founders, the Berlin physician, scientist and politician Rudolf Virchow. As a pathologist, Virchow (Figure 2) worked with the bodies of dead human beings. Through his dissections and microscopic studies, however, his research was geared towards life, to determine the course of disease and to find out more precisely how the living human organism is able to resist or conquer it. He thus arrived at a significant analogy. As a Prussian civil servant and a citizen predisposed to a republican form of government, he demanded during the Revolution of 1848 that a democratic government be formed as a federation of individuals with equal rights. Under the microscope he saw the complex interdependent human tissue in a similar way, as a democratic organism composed of equal but at the same time variously talented individuals: the cells. In his quest to understand the attributes of cells in detail and his search for specific indicators and mechanisms of disease, Virchow established a biological approach for Western medicine that is still largely followed today.[2]

FIGURE 2
Lithograph of Rudolf Virchow
(1821–1902), around 1850.
Photograph © Berlin Museum of
Medical History of the Charité.

VIRCHOW'S IMPACT

Probing into life characterised not only Virchow's approach as a researcher but also his interests as a collector. He began his career as a pathologist at the Berlin Charité Hospital in 1844 and developed an interest in documenting various stages of disease processes using different media: texts, pictures, artificial reproductions, but most of all tangible specimens of the human organism. From 1856 onwards, when he became director of the newly built Institute of Pathology on the premises of the Charité, he aimed to collect a complete inventory of all known diseases of the human body. Until the end of the nineteenth century, he and his assistants prepared thousands of specimens from the many dissections undertaken in his institute. In 1899, Virchow was able to open a Pathological Museum of the Charité, to which he transferred some 23,066 wet and dry specimens (Figure 3). On 12 October 1901, he marked his eightieth birthday by presenting the first arrangement of his specimens to a large international group of senior scientists.[3]

Over a museum exhibition space of 2,000m^2 on five floors, Virchow endeavoured to realise a dynamic exhibition. Above all, he intended his impressive collection of specimens to demonstrate one thing: the typical course or development of particular diseases from the first signs through to the final stages. His aim was to promote visual understanding by comparing distinct tissue alterations in specimens that he placed next to each other on the shelves of the large showcases.[4]

FIGURE 3
Pathological Museum at the Charité around 1900.
Photograph © Berlin Museum of Medical History of the Charité.

TRACING LIFE TODAY

Although arranged differently, the Berlin Museum of Medical History at the Charité now occupies the same building as Virchow's collection and is intended to resonate with his approach (Figure 4). With its 1,400 objects in a space of 800m², the *Tracing Life* exhibition presents inner views of the human body intended to highlight healthy and diseased structures and mechanisms in the living human body. It also presents the perspectives of people with illnesses who have turned to medicine in the hope of help with their recovery.

The exhibition is introduced with the display of a representative spectrum of preserved human organs and bodily structures, specimens that show what is defined as 'normal' anatomy. Beginning in 1700, it asks what anatomists and pathologists have discovered with their knives and microscopes (Figure 5) and to what extent bodily functions have been understood by their colleagues – physicists, physiologists, biologists, and chemists – who, from the mid nineteenth century onward, performed experiments in new medical laboratories (Figure 6). The focus in both dissecting rooms and laboratories was on hearts and brains, muscles and nerves, but also moved to structures and mechanisms in smaller units of life: cells, molecules and genes. In these different ways, light is shed on the functions of bodies in both health and illness. Specimens, models, moulages, instruments, illustrations, diagrams and photographs chronicle specific notions of the body that are bound to the time and setting in which they were formed (Figures 7 and 8). Yet these ideas remain relevant to medicine today – for instance, in attempts to generate three-dimensional reconstructions through digital medical imaging or in investigations of the human brain using different scanning techniques.

FIGURE 4 (ABOVE , LEFT)
Berlin Museum of Medical
History of the Charité, 2012.
Photograph © Christoph Weber.

FIGURE 5 (ABOVE, RIGHT)
Diseased skulls from the oldest
part of the museum's specimen
collection, pre-1800.
Photograph © Thomas Bruns.

FIGURE 6 (BELOW)
A 'kymographion', for physiological
experiments on the patterns of
rhythmic muscle contractions, made
by F Sauerwald in Berlin around 1860.
Photograph © Christoph Weber.

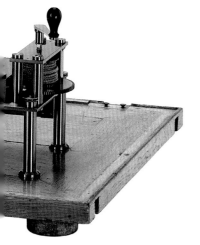

PATHOLOGY ON DISPLAY

The pre-eminent view of the diseased body that physicians and pathologists held in Virchow's time can be understood by taking a closer look at one of the major focal points of the museum: the large specimen hall. Considered to be the core of the museum, this area leaves a lasting impression on its audiences. Each side of the eight original glass showcases is dedicated to an important organ or system in the human body, displayed in its regular shape and function (Figure 9). Further along in the showcases, visitors are confronted by a selection of specimens that demonstrate major diseases that typically attack that particular organ or system (Figures 10 and 11). Finally, diseases relevant to each organ or system, which have presented particular dangers or challenges, are exhibited, such as tuberculosis, kidney stones, heart attacks and brain tumours (Figure 12).

Around 750 specimens from the museum's collection are displayed here: body parts that act as educational documents of physical conditions.[5] But, however informative these may be, this is a sensitive display that can arouse strong emotions in visitors. Some specimens show potentially disturbing malformations

FIGURE 7
Corrosion cast of the vessels of
the upper intestines, 1960.
Photograph © Christoph Weber.

or embryos and foetuses. Others were preserved during a
time when it was not common practice to ask the patient for
consent to keep, prepare, and display his or her organs after
their death. The museum's ethical stance is now in accordance
with recommendations regarding respectful treatment of
human remains held in collections and museums, published in
a prominent German medical journal in 2003.[6] Following these
guidelines, each specimen on display is anonymous, so that
the person to whom they once belonged cannot be identified.
Furthermore, a prominent text in the specimen hall, *In Memoriam*,
informs visitors about the specific ethical and historical contexts
of the specimen collection:

> The Berlin Medical Historical Museum shows a large number
> of wet and dry pathological-anatomical specimens in the
> Rudolf Virchow Hall. The preserved tissue structures usually
> bear direct evidence of illness and wounds. In contrast to the
> practice at the Charité Hospital today, it was not previously

FIGURE 8 (LEFT)
Late 19th-century model
of the human eye.
Photograph © Christoph Weber.

FIGURE 9
Respiratory system display, 2007.
Photograph © Christoph Weber.

*customary to ask permission of patients, in case of their deaths,
to remove and preserve their organs and tissue for the purpose
of research and teaching. Patients were also not specifically
asked if they would be willing to allow the presentation of the
specimens – either in the collections kept for medical personnel
or for interested visitors to the museum. At the Charité a
medical culture of collecting and exhibiting developed during
the nineteenth century that was authoritarian and hierarchically
organised. This culture had an impact outside the boundaries of
the hospital and was generally – as far as we know – approved.
Because the practice of using patients' tissue and organs
without explicit permission was accepted at this time, and
with hindsight was not based on methods that were (wilfully)
disrespectful or actually criminal, the museum has decided
to continue presenting the specimens for the public today. By
unintentionally leaving a 'piece of themselves' the deceased
have done a great service for those who have come after them.
We bow down before all of the individuals who are gathered in
this room through the specimens on exhibition. We remember
them with thankfulness.*

MEDICAL LABORATORIES

The *Tracing Life* exhibition raises questions about the
consequences for patients of research in medical diagnosis
and treatment. It shows how, in the nineteenth century, along
with the development of modern hospitals, knowledge gained
by pathologists through post-mortem examination of the dead
impacted upon clinical practice at the sickbed. For example, by
conducting autopsies they obtained views of diseased hearts and
lungs that helped them to understand and interpret the sounds
heard through a stethoscope held over a patient's chest; and
changes in the respiratory system or bones brought about by
tuberculosis could be linked to visible changes in a patient's
physical condition at the bedside. The exhibition also shows how
surgeons began to incorporate into their surgical procedures

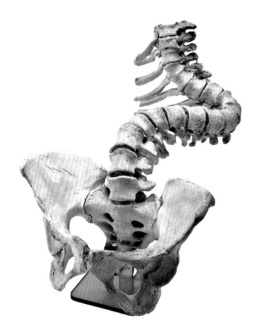

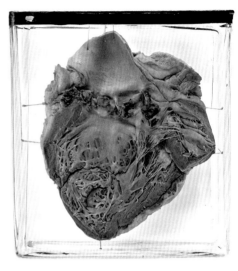

the latest developments in anaesthesia and hygienic measures. In addition, visitors to the museum can discover the importance of specific medical treatments, for example, Emil von Behring's detection of antitoxins (later called antibodies) in blood serum to fight diphtheria, and the manufacture of the drug Salvarsan (also known as arsphenamine) for syphilis, following the laboratory discovery of this compound by Paul Ehrlich in 1909.

A central part of the exhibition focuses on one of twentieth-century medicine's darkest moments: National Socialism. Commonplace medical objects – syringes, operating instruments, medications, microscopes, and textbooks – are displayed to provide insight into customary medical practice in the 1930s and 1940s. And then the same kinds of objects are shown again in a different context. Under the headings of racial hygiene, compulsory sterilisation, experiments on humans and euthanasia, the functions of these objects in realising the goals of inhuman medicine under National Socialism can be seen.

FIGURE 10 (LEFT)
Scoliosis of the backbone, 1894.
Photograph © Christoph Weber.

FIGURE 11 (RIGHT)
Endocarditis (inflammation of the inner murals of the heart), 1957.
Photograph © Christoph Weber.

PATIENT HISTORY

Although much of the *Tracing Life* exhibition follows an expressly medical view based on Virchow's ideas, in certain sections there are conscious efforts to bring people's experiences of illness – or even those of a particular patient – to the fore. Thus a collection of 36 facial wax casts (moulages) is on display (Figure 13). These portraits were taken from the faces of people who were treated in the first decade of the twentieth century at the Charité Eye Clinic. These casts formed a teaching collection, a systematic representation of illnesses that was built up in a hospital where patients were treated within the regimes of new medical specialties, such as ophthalmology and dermatology. In the gallery today, with their specific conditions fixed in wax, the facial expressions of each of those patients reveal the signs of their highly individual physical and emotional reactions.[7] These individual documents of states of suffering are probably the greatest challenge for the museum's visitors, who often view the moulages with mixed sensations of curiosity and disgust, of sympathetic attraction and personal feelings of repulsion. Sometimes seeing themselves in these faces, they ask whether they want to continue to look and to find out more, or to turn away.

Further aspects of people's medical experiences can be seen in a newly developed display modeled on a twentieth-century hospital ward. Unique among German museums, this uses museum objects to show original medical case histories of patients (identified with their first names only, so that their privacy is protected). Based on a 1910 ward in the medical clinic of the Charité (Figure 14), visitors encounter ten beds revealing the stories of people with different medical conditions in the period between 1727 and 2006 (Figure 15).[8] The foot of each bed has been fashioned as a showcase introducing the actual historical individual and the specific medical condition that led her or him to seek help in hospital (usually the Charité). Each mattress has been converted into a base on which there

FIGURE 12
Brain tumours in the nerve structure displays, 1910–1963.
Photograph © Thomas Bruns.

are relevant objects where the patient's world and medicine meet. Finally, the heads of the beds have been constructed as high, glass showcases providing medical knowledge about the individual's illness or condition and how it could be treated at that time. Through this arrangement visitors meet a young pregnant woman in 1727 who experienced the 'difficult birth' of her baby who had been in transverse presentation; a man with fever and malarial symptoms who was helped briefly when china bark was administered to him in 1844; a three-year-old boy with polio who lay for many weeks in an iron lung in 1958, three years before the introduction of oral immunisation for that disease; a highly creative young woman who developed a psychosis and finally took her own life in 1969 after many hospital admissions; a person with liver failure who received a new organ in 1990; and a middle-aged man who got a splinter in his finger shortly before Christmas 2006, developed blood poisoning and, two weeks later, was fighting for his life in intensive care.

LOCATING THE MUSEUM

On the one hand, *Tracing Life* connects with the original function of the Virchow museum building, taking as its starting point

FIGURE 13 (LEFT)
Eye moulages dating to around 1900.
Photograph © Thomas Bruns.

FIGURE 14 (MIDDLE)
Female patients' ward in the 2nd Medical Clinic of the Charité, 1910.
Photograph © Berlin Museum of Medical History of the Charité.

FIGURE 15 (RIGHT)
Historical patients' ward, 2007.
Photograph © Thomas Bruns.

the medical practice of performing anatomical dissections and presenting a scientific understanding of the human body. On the other, it consciously relates to the neighborhood of the museum. From its beginning, the museum has stood in the grounds of the Charité, surrounded by the clinics and institutes of this well-known and respected Berlin hospital. These two aspects are highlighted in the museum's displays, which include showcases detailing the history of the Charité. Visitors' attention is drawn to the founding of the institution in 1710, by the Prussian King Friedrich I, as a plague house outside the city walls, and also to its development from military hospital to university hospital at four different locations in the German capital.[9]

Moving from historical to contemporary medical issues, the museum engages visitors with its displays of a ward and a laboratory. It also addresses technical and ethical dimensions of organ transplantation and the possibilities and limits of technologically intensive medical care. It takes a look behind the scenes of research laboratories for genetics and neuroscience, presenting visitors with purposefully open questions. How far are human beings in their biological, emotional, intellectual and social aspects shaped by organic factors, and how far by cultural influences?

Starting as Virchow's Pathological Museum in 1899, the museum has undergone fundamental changes over time. Serving as an instrument of medical education for both the scientific and general public, it originally relied on the visual effects of, sometimes extreme, pathological specimens. Today it offers visitors a historical narrative as they pass through a sequence of specific medical rooms that present a wide spectrum of medical practices and objects. These are arranged to shed light on medical research, diagnosis and treatment, providing visitors with information as well as inviting them to question medical practices past and present.

Although the museum has a large specialised audience from all medical fields, the main target group is the interested lay public, attracting up to 90,000 visitors a year from all social and professional backgrounds. High school classes (of 16–18-year-olds) often closely examine the displays either by themselves or on a guided tour. Because many specimens on show are found challenging, with strong emotional effects, the museum has a minimum age of 16 years. Younger people are not excluded from the galleries but they must be accompanied by a responsible adult.

In the near future the museum will concentrate on three aspects of its work: developing research with objects from its stores to generate new ideas for special exhibitions; increasing use of its collections and galleries for educational activities, for professionals and the general public; and continuing to open its permanent exhibition to innovative temporary displays, in the form of interventions, which create new dimensions within, and add what is absent from, *Tracing Life*.

NOTES

1. Thomas Schnalke and Isabel Atzl (eds.), *Dem Leben auf der Spur im Berliner Medizinhistorischen Museum der Charité* (München: Prestel Verlag, 2010). The ideas behind the Berlin Museum of Medical History at the Charité have previously been rehearsed in Thomas Schnalke, 'Tracing Life: The History, Concept and Goals of the New Permanent Exhibition in the Berlin Museum of Medical History at the Charité', *Medicina nei Secoli Arte e Scienza*, 21 (2009), 117–140.

2. Erwin H Ackerknecht, *Rudolf Virchow. Arzt, Politiker, Anthropologe* (Stuttgart, Ferdinand Enke Verlag, 1957); Constantin Goschler, *Rudolf Virchow. Mediziner – Anthropologe – Politiker* (Köln: Böhlau Verlag, 2002); Renato G Mazzolini, *Politisch-biologische Analogien im Frühwerk Rudolf Virchows* (Marburg: Basilisken-Presse, 1998).

3. Rudolf Virchow, *Die Eröffnung des Pathologischen Museums der Königlichen Friedrich-Wilhelms-Universität zu Berlin* (Berlin: Verlag von August Hirschwald, 1899); Angela Matyssek, *Rudolf Virchow. Das Pathologische Museum. Geschichte einer wissenschaftlichen Sammlung* (Darmstadt: Steinkopff, 2002).

4. Thomas Schnalke, 'Ohne Sinn und Verstand? Rudolf Virchows Strategie des Sammelns am Beispiel seines Pathologischen Museums', *Acta Historica Leopoldina*, 48 (2007), 217–39.

5. Hans-Jörg Rheinberger, 'Präparate – "Bilder" ihrer selbst. Eine bildtheoretische Skizze', *Bildwelten des Wissens*, 1/2 (2003), 9–19; Thomas Schnalke and Isabel Atzl, 'Magenschluchten und Darmrosetten. Zur Bildwerdung und Wirkmacht pathologischer Präparate', *Bildwelten des Wissens*, 9/1 (2012), 18–28.

6. Arbeitskreis Menschliche Präparate in Sammlungen Arbeitskreis, 'Empfehlungen zum Umgang mit Präparaten aus menschlichem Gewebe in Sammlungen, Museen und öffentlichen Räumen', *Deutsches Ärzteblatt*, 100 (2003), 378–83.

7. Thomas Schnalke, *Diseases in Wax. The History of the Medical Moulage* (Berlin: Quintessence books, 1995); Thomas Schnalke, 'Casting Skin: Meanings for Doctors, Artists, and Patients', in *Models: The Third Dimension of Science*, ed. by Soraya de Chadarevian and Nick Hopwood (Stanford, California. Stanford University Press, 2004), pp. 207–41.

8. *Die Charité in Berlin. Fotografien um 1910*, ed. by Volker Hess (Berlin: Be.Bra, 2010).

9. Petra Lennig, *Die Berliner Charité. Schlaglichter aus 3 Jahrhunderten* (Berlin: Berliner Medizinhistorisches Museum, 2010); *Die Charité. Geschichte(n) eines Krankenhauses*, ed. by Johanna Bleker and Volker Hess (Berlin: Akademie Verlag, 2010).

Biomedicine on display

Copenhagen's Medical Museion

Thomas Söderqvist and Bente Vinge Pedersen

Reflecting recent trends in the study of material culture, the Medical Museion at the University of Copenhagen (Figure 1) has undergone significant changes in the past decade. Initially a huge collection of medico-historical artefacts used mainly for research and teaching purposes, the museum is now carving out an identity as a cross-disciplinary site for understanding medicine in historical, philosophical and cultural terms. Combining academic research in medical humanities, aesthetics, material studies and science communication with experimental exhibition-making, public events and an active web presence, the aim of the museum is to contribute to public engagement with medicine and to highlight how medicine is an active participant in contemporary culture.

A CROWDSOURCED MUSEUM

The museum began a century ago with a burst of collecting frenzy. To celebrate the rise of scientific medicine in the second half of the nineteenth century, a group of Copenhagen physicians decided to create a temporary exhibition in connection with the 50th anniversary of the Danish Medical Association (Den almindelige danske Lægeforening) in 1907. They issued a call to their colleagues to donate medical objects, including instruments,

FIGURE 1 (OPPOSITE)
Medical Museion logo, 2012.

quack remedies, curiosities, healthcare items, portraits and
manuscripts. The result of this massive acquisition enterprise –
which would today be called crowdsourcing – was overwhelming:
thousands of historical artefacts previously stored in the attics
and basements of hospitals and the homes of doctors were
collected. The exhibition, held in the Danish parliament building,
became a public spectacle and the organisers decided that the
many artefacts should be transferred to a newly founded Medical
History Museum (Medicinsk-Historisk Museum) in Copenhagen
(Figure 2).

FIGURE 2
Detail from the founding
exhibition of the Copenhagen
Medical History Museum marking
the 50th anniversary of the
Danish Medical Association.
Unknown photographer, 1907. Medical
Museion Image Collection.

One of the major problems for the new museum owners was to find a permanent space. Although the professor of medical history, Vilhelm Maar, managed to persuade the University of Copenhagen to take over the responsibility for the artefact collection in 1918, it remained in storage for a decade. Lack of space was a constant theme in the annual reports until the late 1920s when Maar succeeded in locating a semi-permanent home and arranged it as a study collection for medical students. It took another half century, however, to open the museum to the general public.

As a consequence of the university takeover, a succession of professors in medical history, all with a strong medical background, served as directors of the museum, and from the 1920s to the 1970s the museum became one of the most advanced research museums and collections of its kind in Europe. Maar was followed by Edvard Gotfredsen, whose *Medicinens historie* (History of Medicine) remained the standard Scandinavian textbook for decades.[1] The museum's academic status was productive. In the mid-1940s the growing collection was moved to its present spacious domicile in the building complex of the former Royal Surgical Academy in Bredgade in central Copenhagen (Figure 3).

The acquisition programme was accelerated under Gotfredsen's curatorship. Over the decades a continuous flow of objects and images from medical science and practice, including surgery, ophthalmology, obstetrics, dentistry, radiology and pharmaceutics, were acquired and as a result the University of Copenhagen today has one of the largest and most diverse collections of artefacts from the history of medicine. There are between 100,000 and 200,000 items, from low-tech nursing equipment to high-tech digitalised apparatus, ranging from the mid-seventeenth to the late twentieth century (Figure 4).

In the late 1960s, Gotfredsen's sucessor, the renowned osteoarchaeologist Vilhelm Møller-Christensen, took the initiative to create the first public galleries, which were officially

FIGURE 3
Cross-section of the Royal Surgical Academy, designed by architect Peter Meyn. The building was inaugurated in 1787. Drawing by unknown artist. The National Museum of Denmark.

opened by the Danish King Frederik IX (Figure 5). After his
retirement in 1973, however, the professorship was put on hold
and the museum gradually drifted into the doldrums. There were
some acquisitions in the 1980s and 1990s, notably thousands
of wet and dry specimens from the university's pathological–
anatomical department and a large collection of teratological
foetuses. But otherwise collecting stopped and research activity
declined; finally, the museum lost its independent status within
the university organisation. Without an active research and
curatorial environment, the public galleries waned. The original
auditorium and demonstration theatre from 1787 remained the
only active part of the museum – and the faculty's preferred
space for dissertation defences and inaugurations of new
medical professors.

In the mid-1990s, however, the faculty decided to restore
the status of the museum and place it organisationally in the new

FIGURE 5
Professor Vilhelm Møller-
Christensen in his study collection
of bones excavated from
medieval leprosy cemeteries.
Unknown photographer, 1970s.
Medical Museion Image Collection.

FIGURE 4 (OPPOSITE, TOP)
Detail from Medical Museion's
dentistry collection, showing
ivory and plastic denture from
the 18th and 19th centuries.
Photograph by Jan Engelhardt, 2003.
Medical Museion Image Collection.

Department of Public Health. Over the following decade the long-
vacant professorship in medical history was filled, PhD students
were recruited, a research seminar established, and the level of
external funding increased significantly. The museum now has
around 20 permanent and temporary faculty and staff members
and half of its budget comes from external sources.

The revival of the museum went hand in hand with a
pronounced identity shift. In 2003, its new direction was heralded
with a new name, Medical Museion, from the Greek 'μουσειον', a
place where the muses inspire intellectual and poetic activities.
Not only a museum of the medical past but also a space for

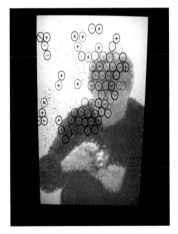

FIGURE 6 (ABOVE)
Autoportrait of the director of Medical
Museion, Thomas Söderqvist, made
from video input to an interactive
installation inspired by the research
methodology of Nobel Prize-winning
scientist John Sulston, created
by British artist Daniel Brown.
Photograph by Thomas Söderqvist, 2008.

FIGURE 7 (RIGHT)
The installation *Avalanches of
Data* from the exhibition *Split +
Splice: Fragments from the Age
of Biomedicine*, 2009–10.
Photograph by Rikke Albrechtsen.
Medical Museion Image Collection.

intellectual and artistic reflection on contemporary and future biomedicine. The new director, the first who had not trained as a clinician (see also Alberti in this volume), argued that the traditional twentieth-century medical museum had played out its role (Figure 6). Developments in biochemistry, molecular and cell biology, in imaging and information technology, and in genetics and genomics, are fundamentally transforming medical research, clinical practice, the pharmaceutical and medical device industries, and not least the status of the patient and the politics of health (biopolitics). A key challenge for medical museums of the twenty-first century is to engage with this major shift toward a global medical system – an engagement that also includes collecting the contemporary heritage from biomedical research institutions, hospitals and clinics.[2]

One of the implications of this new identity is that approaches and methods at the Medical Museion have changed. So, to make sense of the current biomedical revolution and the transformation of the visible and tangible anatomical body into a much more abstract molecular and biopolitical body, it is necessary to employ a more cross-disciplinary approach to medicine. Research and outreach programmes now draw on an array of cultural, social and scientific perspectives, as well as artistic, literary and design practices.

RESEARCH-LED CURATING

Another idea behind the identity shift from medical history museum to Medical Museion was to integrate the three major museum functions: research, outreach and curation.[3] Whereas it has become more common to separate these three basic activities, the founding idea behind the Medical Museion was that it is necessary to integrate them closely – with research as the foundation – in order to engage with the contemporary transformation of medical practices in new and innovative ways. Accordingly, academic staff divide their time between research, curating, exhibition-making and public events.

FIGURE 8
Poster from the exhibition *Split + Splice: Fragments from the Age of Biomedicine* (Danish: *Del og hel: Brudstykker fra biomedicinens tid*), 2009–10. Designed by Lars Møller Nielsen, Studio 8. Medical Museion Archive.

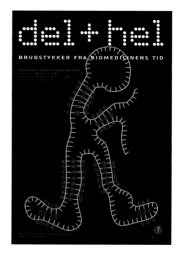

One of the advantages of being a part of the university organisation is that it makes it easier to attract research funding. Medical Museion has secured a number of major grants over the past decade, particularly from the Novo Nordisk Foundation, an independent Danish research foundation with corporate interests in the pharmacological and biotechnology industries, but with no corporate strings attached to its grants. From 2005 to 2009, the foundation supported an integrated research, curatorial and public engagement programme about contemporary Danish biomedicine, entitled Biomedicine on Display, which included research projects on the organisation of organ transplantation, visualisation in epidemiology and endoscopy, and abortion practices and foetus disposal. The four-year grant also included funding for a major public exhibition, *Split + Splice: Fragments from the Age of Biomedicine* (2009), where the exhibition rooms were based on the individual researcher's work and on new acquisitions from regional hospitals and research laboratories (Figures 7 and 8). In 2010, Medical Museion won the Society for the History of Technology's Dibner Award for Excellence in Museum Exhibits for *Split + Splice*.

In 2010, the Novo Nordisk Foundation endowed a new Centre for Basic Metabolic Research at the University of Copenhagen, which includes a Section for Science Communication based at Medical Museion. The aim of the section is to develop public engagement with research on metabolic diseases such as diabetes. Academic research is still the cornerstone for this decade-long communication programme. Like the former programme, the ambition is to integrate it with exhibitions, social media, events and collecting. For example, philosophical research has led the curators and researchers to consider anew the importance of the physical presence of objects in museums.[4] This research informed the exhibitions *Primary Substances: Treasures from the History of Protein Research* (2009) (Figures 9 and 10), *The Chemistry of Life* (2010), which explored metabolic research from the seventeenth century

FIGURE 9
Bottles with peptides and amino acid derivatives used in protein chemistry research at the Carlsberg Laboratory, Copenhagen, in the 1930s–1960s, standing on the shelf before acquisition to Medical Museion in 2010.
Photograph by Thomas Söderqvist.

to the present, (Figure 11) and *Balance and Metabolism* (2011), which contrasts ancient and modern understandings of the body (Figures 12 and 13). This combination of research and exhibition is distinctive and important.

Medical Museion's current director and his colleague at the Wellcome Collection in London drew attention to the close relationship between research and exhibitions in their 2011 manifesto for science, technology and medicine exhibitions: 'Exhibitions should be research-led, not a form of dissemination [...] Curators should use exhibitions to find things out (for themselves and for their visitors) and not just regurgitate what is already known [...] They add their own insights and gradually come up with new ideas and perspectives.'[5] The exhibition *Obesity: What's the Problem?* (2012) about obesity research and gastric bypass surgery exemplifies this approach. The curator–historians and designers went on an investigative journey around the metabolic research laboratories at the University of Copenhagen and operation rooms in the university hospital, and shared their year-long enquiry into the world of obesity research and gastric surgery in an exhibition that raises more questions than answers (Figure 14).

FIGURE 10 (LEFT)
The exhibition *Primary Substances: Treasures from the History of Protein Research*, 2009–10, displayed a handmade enzyme model from the Carlsberg Laboratory in the 1960s against a background of a computer-generated model of the same enzyme from the 2000s. Photograph by Mikael Thorsted.

FIGURE 11 (RIGHT)
Multichannel pipette on display in the exhibition *Chemistry of Life: Four Chapters in the History of Metabolic Research*, 2010. Photograph by Morten Skovgaard. Medical Museion Image Collection.

FIGURE 12 (LEFT)
Detail from the 2011 exhibition
Balance and Metabolism with
pills and tablets that illustrate
the chemical body.
Photograph by Morten Skovgaard.
Medical Museion Image Collection.

FIGURE 13 (RIGHT)
An explanation of the humoural
body in the exhibition *Balance
and Metabolism*, 2011.
Photograph by Morten Skovgaard.
Medical Museion Image Collection.

The outreach programme at Medical Museion also includes experimenting with new forms of public events, including an event series entitled *Close Encounters of a Material Kind* that focuses on the sensuous material aspects of medical research and museum objects. For example, at an event on personalised genomics, the audience circulated between working stations representing the material steps in the calculation of genetic risk: from tissue sampling, via processes such as DNA extraction and DNA sequencing, to genomic data interpretation. Both old and new museum objects were used to show how personalised genomics is not just about abstract gene sequences but a very material and tangible process involving tissue samples, chemical substances, and instruments (Figure 15).

Throughout the past decade, the interaction of research with other museum activities has changed the direction of Medical Museion's research programme. In the early 2000s, the research was exclusively historically oriented; ten years later it is much more varied, drawing on science and technology studies, communication studies, visual and material culture studies, aesthetic philosophy, and design studies. Also, material objects and their immediate sensory presence have been put in the centre of curatorial attention – the display of artefacts is supported by sparse textual descriptions rather than by elaborate storytelling (Figure 16). The exhibition philosophy is to let the artefacts take centre stage at the expense of texts.[6]

Museums are increasingly exploiting the potential of social media for research, curatorship and public engagement. Medical Museion has put strong emphasis on social media as integral to its activities; the museum's blog is currently one of the most visited and cited medical museum blogs in the world.[7] The research and exhibition programme for medical science communication includes a web specialist, who implements new social media platforms not primarily as a means for branding and advertising but rather as instruments for daily research, curatorial work, exhibition-making, event-planning, and as an internal archive. Social media is thus used not only for popular outreach but also as a platform for developing ideas and innovative museum practices, such as reporting on work during the construction of new exhibitions.

The integration of museum functions has proven to have several advantages. First, basic research has not only provided the necessary intellectual background for acquisitions and exhibitions making but also installed a culture of enquiry and curiosity within the museum staff as a whole. Second, the handling and care of artefacts has not only been a precondition for exhibitions, and sometimes an inspiration for new research projects, but also has served as a reminder of the material foundations of medicine and its 'thingness', thereby questioning a widespread assumption in popular culture that science is primarily about theories, facts and social interaction.[8] Finally, exhibitions and events have added a dimension of purpose and tangibility to the scholarly work of the researchers.

COLLECTING FOR THE FUTURE

Medical exhibitions and events are high-profile, public engagement activities that currently appeal to both funding

FIGURE 14
A common scale measures up to 150kgs; to weigh a very obese person you need two weights. Installation from the 2012 exhibition *Obesity: What's the Problem?* Photograph by Ane Pilegaard Sørensen. Medical Museion Image Collection.

FIGURE 15 (RIGHT)
Detail from the event series
*Close Encounters of the Material
Kind* demonstrating the use
of a PCR (polymerase chain
reaction) apparatus in 2012.
Photograph by Bente Vinge Pedersen.
Medical Museion Image Collection.

FIGURE 16 (BELOW)
Detail from the room *The Signs
of Ageing in Oldetopia: On Age
and Ageing*, 2007–2008
Photograph by Laura Stamer. Medical
Museion Image Collection.

agencies and major political and scientific decision-makers; similarly, as the biomedical revolution unfolds, research in the history, philosophy and social studies of medicine will hopefully continue to be fundable. But exhibitions, events and research do not help solve what is maybe the most serious problem facing today's medical museums: how to collect and preserve the biomedical heritage? As former director of the British Museum Robert Anderson pointed out, new acquisitions are 'the lifeblood of museums'.[9]

Collecting and curating the heritage of contemporary biomedicine is not an easy task. First, the volume of new research, clinical objects and (increasingly electronic) documents and images produced is accelerating to the extent that it seems impossible to try to preserve and curate even minor parts of this heritage for the future. Second, scientists and clinicians generally have very little awareness of the heritage value of their artefacts and museums therefore rarely receive spontaneous donations of contemporary artefacts from scientists – not even significant objects from major biomedical breakthroughs. Finally, it is difficult to convince funding agencies of the importance of collecting and curating current medical things. As a consequence, the material heritage of the contemporary biomedical revolution risks becoming lost for the future.

Inspired by citizen science initiatives, which draw on the help of the public to solve real scientific problems,[10] Medical Museion's suggestion for solving the future acquisition problem is to revive the crowdsourcing spirit of the founding collection in 1907. At that time, only medical doctors were involved in acquiring and curating. Now, the task is rather to train clinicians, general practitioners, scientists, medical engineers, nurses and patients to become 'citizen curators'.[11] This tentative solution thus does not try to solve the acquisition problem inside the walls of the physical museum but instead takes curatorial activities out to hospitals, clinics, research laboratories and homes, with the aim of creating a broad awareness and enthusiasm within society for the preservation of present and future biomedical heritage. The Medical Museion of the future may then become a 1907 foundation movement redux but this time as a contribution to a broader biopolitical awareness.

NOTES

1. Edvard Gotfredsen, *Medicinens historie* (Copenhagen: Nyt Nordisk Forlag Arnold Busck, 1950).

2. Thomas Söderqvist, 'Who's Afraid of the Recent Biomedical Heritage?', *Opuscula Musealia*, 15 (2006), 99–105.

3. Medical Museion's work in the last eight years can be followed on the integrated blog and website www.museion.ku.dk.

4. Thomas Söderqvist, Adam Bencard and Camilla Mordhorst, 'Between Meaning Culture and Presence Effects: Contemporary Biomedical Objects as a Challenge to Museums', *Studies in History and Philosophy of Science, Series A*, 40 (2009), 431–38; Thomas Söderqvist and Adam Bencard, 'Do things talk?' in *The Exhibition as Product and Generator of Knowledge*, ed. by Helmuth Trischler et al. (Berlin: Max Planck Institute for History of Science, 2010), pp. 92–102.

5. Ken Arnold and Thomas Söderqvist, 'Back to basics', *Museums Journal*, 111 (2011), 22–27 (p. 24).

6. Thomas Söderqvist, 'Making Sense or Sensing the Made? Research into Presence Production in Museums of Science, Technology and Medicine', in *Research and Museums*, ed. by Svante Lindqvist et al. (Stockholm: Nationalmuseum, 2008), pp. 161–73.

7. Founded in 2005 as Biomedicine on Display the blog is now called Medical Museion: www.mm.ku.dk.

8. Ken Arnold and Thomas Söderqvist, 'Medical Instruments in Museums: Immediate Impressions and Historical Meanings', *Isis*, 102 (2011), 718–29.

9. Josie Appleton, 'I prefer paternalism to populism' (interview with Robert Anderson)', *Spiked Culture* 17 July 2002 (www.spiked-online.com/Articles/00000006D983.htm).

10. See for example Fold.it (www.fold.it) and Galaxy Zoo (www.galaxyzoo.org).

11. Thomas Söderqvist, 'The Participatory Museum and Distributed Curatorial Expertise', *NTM Zeitschrift für Geschichte der Wissenschaften, Technik und Medizin*, 18 (2010), 69–78.

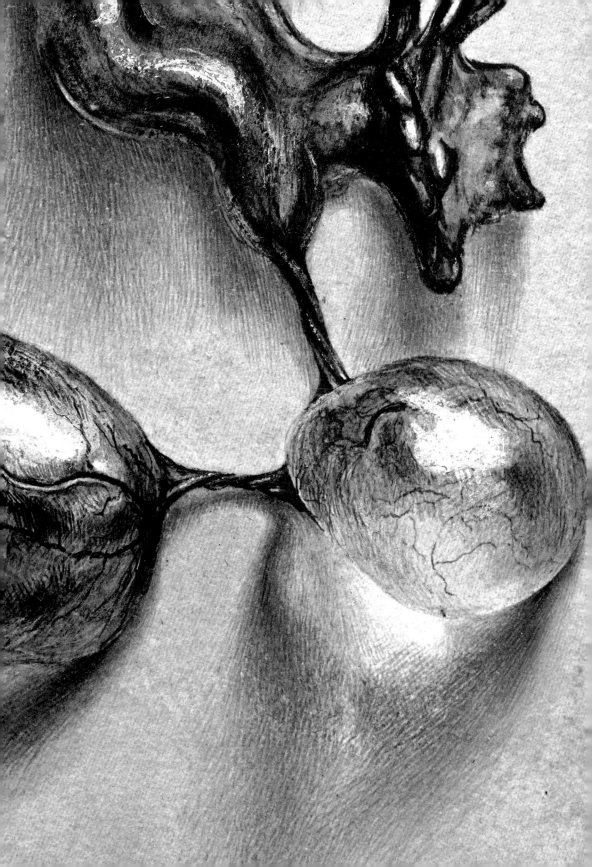

The Dittrick

From doctors' museum to medical history centre

James M Edmonson

The Dittrick Medical History Center and Museum originated as a historical collection chiefly about doctors and the medical profession. The surgeon–founder of the museum collected artefacts with the aim of documenting the advance of medical sciences and associated instruments and technologies. The original celebratory function has in recent years grown more analytical, informed as it is by the historian's approach to studying and making sense of the medical past. The Dittrick now scrutinises the complex formation of professional identity and the physician–patient encounter from historical and cultural perspectives. This chapter addresses how the interpretation of recently acquired collections of artefacts and images has opened opportunities to engage broader audiences, including more students and non-medical museum visitors.

The Dittrick's mission to preserve and celebrate the medical past began in the late 1890s when the Cleveland Medical Library Association (CMLA) established a historical committee. Under the direction of its founder, Dr Dudley Peter Allen, the committee acquired rare medical books and artefacts and over time this collection became the Dittrick Museum. When Allen died in 1915, he bequeathed a sum to endow the fledgling medical

museum. Elizabeth Severance Allen subsequently offered
to fund the building of a new home for the CMLA collections,
laying the foundations for a library and museum in memory of
her husband. This reflected Dr Allen's passion for collecting
medical and surgical antiques and reaffirmed his belief that the
study and display of artefacts could provide important insights
into medical heritage. All this came to fruition when Robert E
Vinson, President of Western Reserve University, offered a tract
of land for the proposed building on the medical campus of the
university. In keeping with the wishes of Mrs Allen, the Allen
Memorial Medical Library (Figure 1) included a museum gallery
occupying its third floor.

When the Allen Library opened its doors in 1926, the CMLA
trustees asked Howard Dittrick (Figure 2), a medical editor and
gynaecologist, to curate their Museum of Historical and Cultural
Medicine. What started as a hobby became a life-long passion

FIGURE 1
Allen Memorial Medical
Library, interior, 2000.
Dittrick Medical History Center.

FIGURE 2
Howard Dittrick, 1946.
Dittrick Medical History Center.

for Dittrick, and indeed in 1944 the museum was named in his honour rather than Allen's. In the first few years he visited major European medical history museums and engaged with their curators, notably Dr GA Wehrli (Zurich University Museum of Medical History), LWG Malcolm (Wellcome Historical Medical Museum), and CJS Thompson (The Royal College of Surgeons of England). Over the next three decades Dittrick avidly collected medical and surgical artefacts, creating a 'doctors' museum' to venerate the scientific and humanitarian achievements of the medical profession. Fortunately for today's visitors, Dittrick collected at a time when such artefacts had more nostalgic than monetary value, so that they were attractive to men in Dittrick's position as well as affordable. By the time of his death in 1954, he had amassed, almost entirely by donation rather than purchase, the most extensive collection of medical technology in North America – larger at the time than that of the Smithsonian (see Chelnick in this volume).

Since 1960 the Dittrick Museum has been directed and curated by historians of medicine. Emphasis has shifted from medical hagiography – uncritically venerating great men – to broader social and cultural aspects of medicine and its technology (see Söderqvist and Pedersen in this volume), with increasing focus upon the patient experience and the physician–patient relationship. The Dittrick has progressively shifted from simply acquiring objects from the medical past to interpreting them in a broader context. The exhibits demonstrate how the experience of medicine and medical care in America is particularly driven by market forces and an implicit faith in more complex technology.

These displays have engaged new audiences beyond the ranks of local doctors. More than ever before, staff at the Dittrick Medical History Center and Museum (as it was formally named in 1998) interact with students in the medical humanities, medicine and nursing, as well as specialists and medical illustrators. These collections have also precipitated research and publication, which have been at the core of the

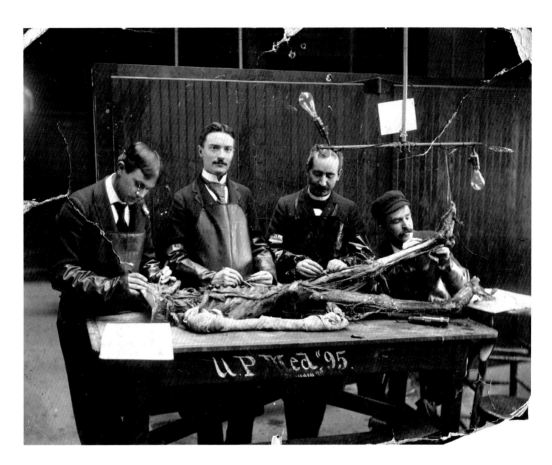

FIGURE 3
A portrait of students in a dissection
class at University of Pennsylvania,
Philadelphia, around 1896.
Dittrick Medical History Center.

museum's mission since the 1966 affiliation with Case Western Reserve University, a major research-oriented university. Since 1998 the Dittrick has been an interdisciplinary study centre of the university, producing exhibitions and publications, and its collections form a resource for students and faculty to employ in research, teaching, and related programming.

Three areas of interest, each with recent museum acquisitions at its core, dominate present exhibitions at the Dittrick and will form the basis of the rest of this chapter: anatomy, within which there is a focus on the role of dissection in the formation of professional identity in medicine, as well as on medical illustration; reproductive health, encompassing conception, childbirth and contraception; and finally, the issue of physical examination in medical encounters, which includes the role of technology in medicine and its impact upon the physician–patient relationship.

ANATOMY

From its inception, the Dittrick benefited from strong anatomical collections; indeed, the very first book given to the library was a 1555 edition of Andreas Vesalius's influential book on human anatomy, *De humani corporis fabrica*. Complementing this foundation are two anatomy-related collections: photographs of medical students posing for their portraits with the cadavers they were dissecting, 1844–1950; and the anatomical art collection of HF Aitken. These collections provide rich documentation of anatomy as ritual, and a glimpse of medical and surgical illustration from the past.

The collection of dissection class portraits evokes the seminal rite of passage in medical students' lives (Figure 3), which helped transform them from lay people to medical professionals. Seen in isolation, one of these images can now seem a macabre expression of students' ghoulish perversity but when seen in a great number, however, it becomes clear that these images were social documents that recorded the formation of professional identity and spoke to medical students' attitudes toward death and the body. These images document an objectification of the body by students and the dark humour they espoused as a way to emotionally distance and steel themselves from the fact that the cadaver was once a sentient, feeling individual.

This genre of medical group portraiture blossomed with the advent of photography and lasted almost a century. It came to an abrupt end in 1950, however, when programmes for members of the public to donate their own bodies were initiated and when, at the same time, there developed a new sense of dignity and respect concerning these deceased bodies donated for teaching anatomy. In 1998 the Dittrick was offered the largest known collection of such images, which were exhibited

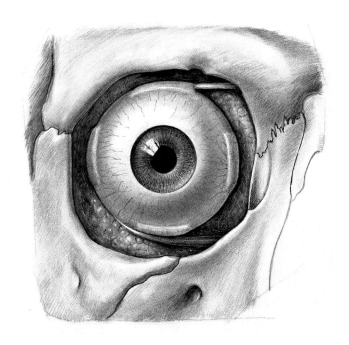

FIGURE 4
Anatomical drawing by
HF Aitken, 1910.
Dittrick Medical History Center.

the following year and later published as a book.[1] In this, as in so many projects dealing with sensitive material, viewing the images within their historical setting was crucial and audience response was overwhelmingly favourable. The book spoke to medical professionals, who had endured dissection classes as students. For others, the book publically reveals a formerly secretive world, rife with proscribed practices permitted only to members of the profession.

The Dittrick also boasts the HF Aitken collection of biomedical art, more than 2,000 sketches, drawings, paintings, prints, and books from the estate of Hamlet Frederick Aitken, an artist and medical illustrator from Boston, Massachusetts. The Aitken collection reveals the emergence of professional biomedical illustration for surgical and medical purposes around 1900 in medical centres such as Baltimore, Boston, and

Cleveland (Figures 4 and 5). During his career, Aitken worked with major figures in American surgery, including Harvey Cushing, the pre-eminent neurosurgeon at Harvard, as well as the leading medical illustrator Max Brödel at Johns Hopkins University. Through Aitken's illustrations current viewers are able to witness the work of a medical artist in compelling detail, and to understand better the history of American medical illustration. Indeed, medical media from many periods are found in the collection: pencil sketches, charcoal renderings, pen and ink sketches, some with colour wash, the laborious carbon dust technique (preferred by Max Brödel), and various printed images. Aitken's choice and mastery of technique can be seen along with the development of particular styles of anatomical illustration.

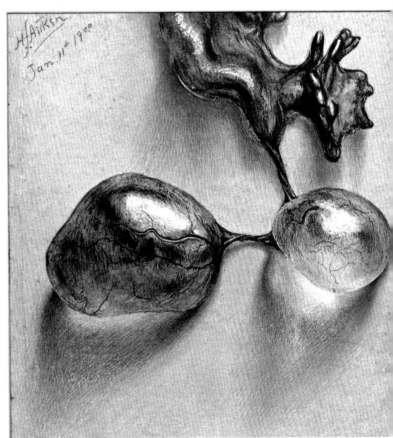

FIGURE 5
Anatomical painting by HF Aitken, 1900, listed as a possible neurofibroma (a benign tumour on a nerve). Dittrick Medical History Center.

REPRODUCTIVE HEALTH

That the Dittrick's mission was directed towards exploration of patients' experiences as well as those of clinicians' is evidenced by the approach taken with the Skuy Collection of historic contraceptive devices, acquired in 2004.[2] This involved community outreach and new collaborations with on-campus groups, which were conducted with awareness of the sensitivities surrounding this subject, especially in the US. (The Dittrick is aligned with Planned Parenthood and other bodies that provide greater access to contraception, especially to financially disadvantaged persons.)

Percy Skuy first started collecting contraceptive devices in 1965, while a product manager in Toronto, Canada, for Ortho Pharmaceuticals (now Janssen Pharmaceuticals, Inc). Before long he started displaying the contraceptives in an exhibition space at the headquarters of Ortho Pharmaceuticals, and over the next four decades Skuy created the largest collection of its kind in the world (Figures 6, 7 and 8).

In 2004, Skuy gifted his collection to the Dittrick, where it is housed in its own Skuy Gallery. The exhibition of the collection has an avowedly American-specific focus rather than attempting general worldwide coverage. This opened in September 2009, entitled *Virtue, Vice and Contraband: A History of Contraception in America* (Figure 9). It is organised into sections demarcated by pivotal events concerning access to or knowledge about contraception: publication of Charles Knowlton's *Fruits of Philosophy* (1832), the first printed American work on contraception; the Comstock Act (1873) that criminalised contraception; the advent of Margaret Sanger's birth control clinics (1915); and the introduction of oral contraceptives (1960).

The opening of the Skuy Gallery has since inspired a fresh approach to the Dittrick's main gallery space, and a reconfiguration of displays has begun with new components relating to reproductive health. In particular, a gallery section is devoted to the history of childbirth, drawing on the museum's

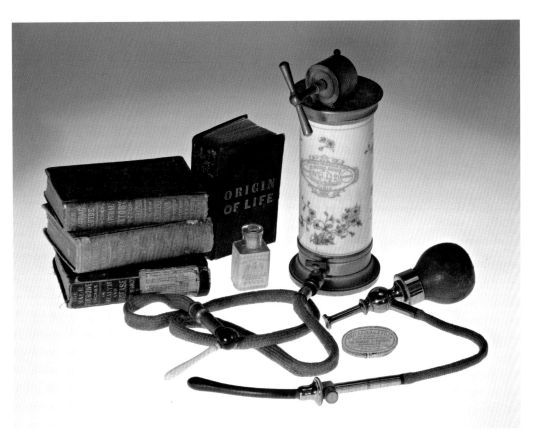

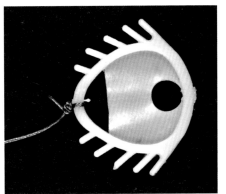

FIGURE 9
Virtue, Vice and Contraband in
the Skuy Gallery, 2009.
Dittrick Medical History Center.

strengths in obstetrics and recently acquired materials on midwifery, such as an eighteenth-century midwifery mannequin (Figure 10). The sheer bulk of the collection – hundreds of contraceptive artefacts – forms overwhelming evidence of persistent and creative efforts to control fertility and conception.

PHYSICAL EXAMINATION AND DIAGNOSTIC INSTRUMENTS

Medical technology and instrumentation have always featured strongly at the Dittrick; its collection began in 1897 with the donation of the extensive surgical instrument armamentarium of surgeon Gustav Weber.[3] To this Dr Allen added his own instruments, and those of Ohio doctors, so that the nascent collection numbered over 2,000 items at the time of Allen's death in 1915. Howard Dittrick built upon this strength when he became curator, avidly acquiring obsolete surgical instruments and furnishings, and a comprehensive array of nineteenth-century diagnostic instrumentation (including stethoscopes, otoscopes, ophthalmoscopes and sphygmomanometers). Obstetrics and gynaecology, Dittrick's own area of expertise, are especially well represented (300 forceps and instruments for extracting the foetus, 150 vaginal speculae and related gynaecological surgery instruments); his wider collection eventually included over 30,000 items (Figure 11).

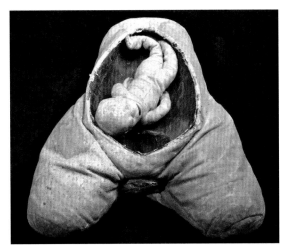

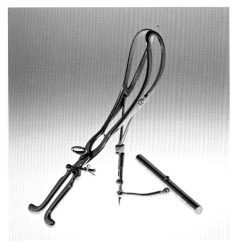

FIGURE 10 (LEFT)
French obstetric manikin
from around 1800.
Dittrick Medical History Center.

FIGURE 11 (RIGHT)
Tarnier axis traction obstetric
forceps, around 1925, marked
'Kny-Scheerer/Germany'.
Dittrick Medical History Center.

The addition of the American Society for Gastrointestinal Endoscopy (ASGE) collection in 1989 and the M Donald Blaufox collection of diagnostic instruments in 2008–2009 each precipitated notable new projects, publications and exhibitions at the Dittrick, with an emphasis upon the role of technology in the physician–patient encounter (Figures 12, 13 and 14). The ASGE instrument collection and associated archives have been used in a number of ways: to compose a history of the ASGE; to document the development of instrumentation for gastrointestinal endoscopy; and to develop a travelling exhibit for ASGE meetings.[4] Equally important, this collection became a catalyst for broadening the international cooperation and collaboration with Hans J Reuter, a distinguished urologist, inveterate endoscope collector and co-author of the encyclopaedic *History of Endoscopy* (1999). Reuter's collection ultimately found a home at the Josephinum (University of Vienna), and cordial ties have been forged with the Dittrick. There has also been collaboration with the William P Diddusch Center for Urologic History at the American Urological Association in Baltimore as the collections of both institutions feature endoscopy as a notable strength.

Blaufox had already donated a collection of 130 drawings of stethoscopes from the estate of medical collector Nolie Mumey, when in 2009 he also gave his own collection of instruments

for auscultation (stethoscopes) and sphygmomanometry (blood pressure determination) to the Dittrick.[5] This gift, numbering over 150 pieces, constituted a landmark addition. Indeed, the arrival of the Blaufox collection initiated a complete revamp of the gallery of diagnostic instruments, to be completed in 2013. In the process, the meanings and importance of instruments – not just as tools but as cultural icons and professional symbols, like the stethoscope or the head mirror (used to examine ears, nose and throat) – were highlighted. The exhibition explores the roots of physical examination with instruments in medical practices and traces the development of this medical routine and ritual. Images of doctors conducting physical examinations proved particularly helpful in telling this story, and in relating it to the experiences of museum visitors, who today are not limited to doctors and nursing and medical students, but now include a broad spectrum of the museum-going public, most without a medical or health-science background.

The Dittrick has recently attracted several notable new collections, enriching an already extensive base of artefacts, rare books and images. These collections were assembled

FIGURE 12 (LEFT)
Modified Laennec stethoscope, around 1830, from the Blaufox diagnostic instrument collection. Dittrick Medical History Center.

FIGURE 13 (RIGHT)
Rogers sphygmomanometer, around 1920, from the Blaufox diagnostic instrument collection. Dittrick Medical History Center.

by passionate individuals who are now anxious to see their collecting efforts preserved intact. The museum goes beyond the mere fulfilment of stewardship, however, to derive meaning from things collected through exhibitions and associated activities. In the process, it retains its focus on important medical matters: anatomy and the body; gestation and birth; physical examination and doctor–patient relations. These are not timeless issues. Rather, they are socially constructed and mediated, continually changing over time. Revealing to museum visitors how this transpires is at the heart of the museum's mission to explore and explicate the medical past. In the end, this endeavour highlights the significance of these collections and perhaps also helps explain why collecting becomes so compelling.

NOTES

1. John Harley Warner and James M Edmonson, *Dissection: Photographs of a Rite of Passage in American Medicine, 1880–1930* (New York: Blast, 2009).

2. Percy Skuy, *Tales of Contraception: A Museum of Discovery* (Toronto: History of Contraception Museum, 1995); Andrea Tone, *Devices and Desires: A History of Contraceptives in America* (New York: Hill and Wang, 2000); Helen Horowitz, *Rereading Sex: Battles over Sexual Knowledge and Suppression in Nineteenth-Century America* (New York: Vintage, 2002).

3. James M Edmonson, *Nineteenth Century Surgical Instruments: A Catalogue of the Gustav Weber Collection* (Cleveland, Ohio: Cleveland Health Sciences Library, 1986); James M Edmonson, *American Surgical Instruments: An Illustrated History and Directory of Instrument Makers to 1900* (San Francisco: Norman, 1997).

4. James M Edmonson, 'History of the instruments for gastrointestinal endoscopy', *Gastrointestinal Endoscopy*, 37 (1991), 27–56; Irvin Modlin, *A Brief History of Endoscopy* (Milan: Multimed, 2000).

5. M Donald Blaufox, *Blood Pressure Measurement: An Illustrated History* (New York: Parthenon, 1998); M Donald Blaufox, *An Ear to the Chest: The Evolution of the Stethoscope* (New York: Parthenon, 2002).

FIGURE 14
Percussion and reflex
hammers, 1850–1930.
Dittrick Medical History Center.

The disturbingly informative Mütter Museum

Robert D Hicks

An outdoor banner promises a 'disturbingly informative' experience to visitors entering one of the most famous museums of pathological anatomy in the United States, the Mütter Museum of the College of Physicians of Philadelphia. Inside, exhibits challenge visitors' perceptions of their own bodies and their expectations of mortality. Skeletons, foetuses in jars, dye-injected organs, and books bound in human skin can disorient and confuse, a sensation captured by Argentine poet and flâneur of the imagined landscape of our lives, Jorge Luis Borges:

I who am singing these lines today
Will be tomorrow the enigmatic corpse
Who dwells in a realm, magical and barren,
Without a before or an after or a when.[1]

Medical museums with anatomical specimens in glass cases differ from other museums in that visitors look at the dead while the dead look back. The most toured small museum in Philadelphia, the Mütter Museum has experienced increasing numbers of visitors – now over 130,000 annually – because a meander through its nineteenth-century vitrines engages visitors with the enigma of mortality. Visitors sense a threshold as they

IMAGE (OPPOSITE)
Detail from Figure 8.

scrutinise a deformed spine, syphilitic skull, or anencephalic foetus and then pause, wordlessly, to recover themselves from a mortal realm that does not seem to have 'a before or after or a when'. Visitors experience dislocation because the specimens on display represent arrested lives, bodies seemingly resisting decay and disappearance. The comments book records the brief encounters with sights not originally intended for public spectacle: 'awesome', 'cool', or even expressions of anxiety such as 'I will take better care of my body after seeing these specimens!'

Enigmatic corpses, models of body parts and the instruments that probe bodies lurk within the century-old Beaux Arts building that houses the college (Figure 1). Near the 'disturbingly informative' banner, visitors read a plaque stating that the college is a national landmark, 'the Birthplace of American Medicine'[SM] – which embodies the historical medical legacy of Philadelphia and its numerous firsts in the US: first medical school, first hospital, first school of optometry, first medical college for women, first school of pharmacy, first children's hospital, first hospital dedicated to the eye, and more. The edginess of the museum's 'disturbingly informative' nature is part of the legacy of the late Gretchen Worden (1947–2004) whose thirty-year tenure as museum curator and director saw visits increase from hundreds annually to tens of thousands. Worden became a talkshow television guest, by turns droll and impish in promoting a scientific medical collection as a locus of popular culture. The Mütter Museum has become a cultural landmark for an audience that extends well beyond the medical cognoscenti (Figure 2). Most visitors are between 18 and 35 years old with very diverse educational and professional backgrounds. Students and professionals in health and medicine come but they are outnumbered by general visitors.

Despite increasing visits, the college faced closure in 2005 for financial reasons. Since 2006, however, under the leadership of a new executive director, George Wohlreich MD, the college

FIGURE 1 (ABOVE)
Mütter Museum brochure cover, 2012.
The College of Physicians of Philadelphia.

has been building its financial capital, seeking grants, and announcing its presence in new areas. For example, Philadelphia high school students have been brought to the college for extracurricular activities to inspire interest in pursuing health careers (Figure 3). Because of harsh economic realities, Wohlreich combined the administration of the museum and Historical Medical Library under one director, a decision which recognises both collections as cultural resources and invites a holistic vision of the collections as a resource for the medical humanities. The decision acknowledges realities in other areas of institutional change: special collections libraries, for instance, are refashioning themselves because digital technologies have democratised and changed patterns of access to sources and scholarship.

ORIGIN AND DEVELOPMENT

The college has grown with the nation and the combined
experiences of its fellowship embrace public health crises,
innovations, philosophies and trends in medicine over the history
of the United States. Founded in 1787 by physicians, including
a signatory of the Declaration of Independence, Benjamin Rush
MD, the college aimed to raise the competence and standing
of physicians and to relieve human suffering. The fellows,
accomplished physicians who are elected to fellowship by
their peers, remain at the core of the college and now number
over 1,400. In 1849, fellow Isaac Parrish MD, a surgeon at
Philadelphia's Wills Hospital (specialising in the eye) proposed
the establishment of a museum of pathological anatomy and to
this end began to collect specimens. Later, in 1858, the college
accepted Dr Thomas Dent Mütter's collection of approximately
1,700 specimens and models that he had used in teaching
surgery at Jefferson Medical College. His bequest of $30,000
generated annual interest that supported a curator's salary and
enabled new purchases (Figure 4).[2]

Mütter described his collections as 'pathological and
anatomical preparations and specimens illustrative of surgery
and medicine, drawings, models, casts, and other like matters',
which formed the eponymous museum.[3] By 1874, the college
resolved to begin collecting rare and curious instruments for
the museum, which spurred growth until 1927 when dwindling
investment became inadequate to support acquisitions. Since
then, the museum has accepted donated materials with the
occasional purchase made from funds raised for the purpose.
The college collections created in 1935 to complement the
specimens and instruments include 'objects of artistic, historic
and scientific interest' in some way associated with important
people in medicine (Figure 5).[4]

Much of the original Mütter collection of skeletons,
models, medical instruments, and various prepared specimens
for study and instruction, remain on display. Now, the museum

FIGURE 4
Thomas Dent Mütter MD,
carte de visite, late 1850s.
The College of Physicians of Philadelphia.

contains about 25,000 items with well-defined collecting foci; approximately 12% of the collection is on display. Unusual institutional survivors – the museum's nineteenth-century vitrines and cabinets – contribute to its historical ambiance. To some degree, then, the Mütter is a museum of itself, although its collections remain vital for current historic and scientific research (Figure 6).

The permanent exhibit contains specimens that many people return to visit as though they are old acquaintances. The tallest skeleton in North America (7'6", 230cm) stands alongside Mary Ashberry, who lived with achondroplasia (the most common cause of dwarfism). The conjoined livers of the twins, Chang and Eng Bunker (1811–1874), reside underneath a plaster cast of the twins, produced post-autopsy (Figure 7). A display on the assassination of Abraham Lincoln includes tissue removed from assassin John Wilkes Booth. The most expensive acquisition in the museum's history – 139 skulls in the Hyrtl Skull

FIGURE 5 (LEFT)
Still life of skulls, trephination instruments, and text from the Mütter Museum collection.
Andrea Baldeck.

FIGURE 6 (RIGHT)
19th-century wax model of a face showing leprosy by Joseph Towne.
Evi Numen, the College of Physicians of Philadelphia.

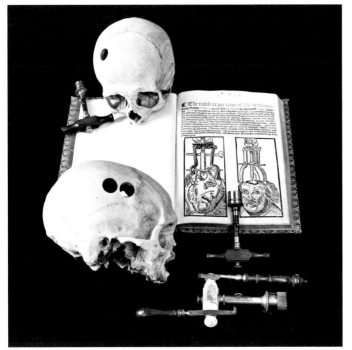

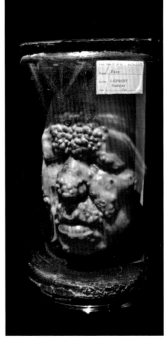

Collection – faces the viewer. In the 1850s, anatomist Josef Hyrtl MD created this collection and inscribed each skull with information then of scientific interest: name, occupation, cause of death, age, birthplace and religion, data that now constitute brief and poignant life histories. Assembled at a time when notions of racial origins and the evolution of humankind were gathering scientific and political currency, Hyrtl's collection was intended to contribute to the debate (Figure 8). Opposite a collection of teratology ('monstrous births'), the tools of Chevalier Jackson, pioneering bronchoesophagologist (a specialist concerned with air passages and the oesophagus), surmount drawers of hundreds of swallowed objects recovered without surgery. Some of the museum specimens on display were acquired under circumstances that would be deemed illegal or unethical today, but the museum is alert to these issues and deals with its collection in an appropriate and sensitive manner.

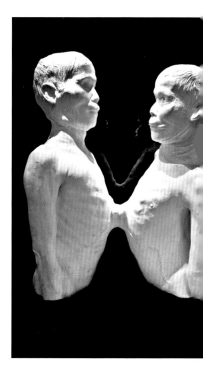

FIGURE 7
Post-mortem plaster cast
of the conjoined torsos of
Chang and Eng Bunker.
Evi Numen, the College of
Physicians of Philadelphia.

BEING HUMAN

Although the museum's collections have been used for teaching and research throughout its history, public visitors began arriving in increasing numbers from the early 1980s. At the museum people see what they cannot see at most other museums: they can explore, intimately and viscerally, aspects of what it means to be human.

The scientific exploration of the museum collection has attracted geneticists, biologists, anthropologists and forensic pathologists. Researchers from a joint project of the University of Toronto and McMaster University recently removed samples of nineteenth-century cholera tissues from museum specimens in a search for viable cholera DNA. This research aims to map cholera epidemics worldwide during the course of two centuries through mathematical models of genetic variation, and no preserved nineteenth-century specimen has yielded viable DNA – until now. One Mütter Museum sample produced the desired result. The museum's Hyrtl skulls have also preoccupied

FIGURE 8
Skulls collected by anatomist
Josef Hyrtl (1810–1894).
Evi Numen, the College of
Physicians of Philadelphia.

researchers. Following the end of civil war in former Yugoslavia in the 1990s, war crimes investigators studied Croat skulls in the collection to help identify anonymous victims of mass murder.

Some recent exhibits have highlighted public health challenges. In response to a request from the City of Philadelphia to complement its public health programme to reduce lead poisoning, the museum created an exhibit, *The Devouring Element: Lead's Impact on Health* (2008), which featured library and museum collections to explore people's love–hate relationship with lead since antiquity. The exhibit aimed to illuminate current public health challenges through dialogue with the past.

In 2013, the 150th anniversary both of the Battle of Gettysburg during the American Civil War and of the Mütter Museum's opening, there is an important new permanent exhibit. *Broken Bodies, Suffering Spirits: Injury, Death, and Healing in Civil War Philadelphia* features an unusual approach to the war's socio-medical dimension. It focuses on the body,

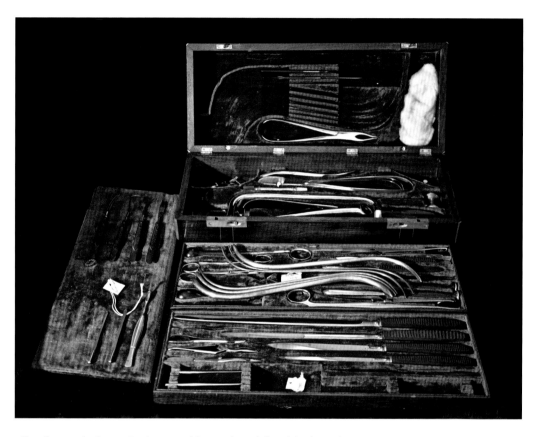

affording an intimate look at a white male soldier, black male
soldier and white female nurse. The exhibit argues that, during
the war, injury, recovery, and death were managed in new ways
and that the war changed American people's relationships with
their own minds and bodies. For instance, visitors will discover
how the emblematic surgery of the war – amputation – was
accomplished and recovery managed; they will also learn why
clinical findings about nerve damage were reported first in
fiction and how phantom limbs related to spiritual séances and
an understanding of electricity (Figure 9).

FIGURE 9
Surgical and amputating kit
presented in 1863 to Dr C T Morton
by soldiers of Ward F, #1 USA
Hospital, Chester, Pennsylvania.
Evi Numen, the College of
Physicians of Philadelphia.

MANY INTERPRETATIONS

Museum objects and specimens, then, simultaneously invite
artistic study, scientific evaluation and public fascination. One

FIGURE 10 (TOP)
Skeleton of Harry Eastlack (1933–
1973) showing fusion caused by
fibrodysplasia ossificans progressiva.
Evi Numen, the College of
Physicians of Philadelphia.

FIGURE 11 (BOTTOM)
Harry Eastlack in 1953, by which
time his disease caused his jaws
to clench, rendering his teeth
inaccessible for dental care.
The College of Physicians of Philadelphia.

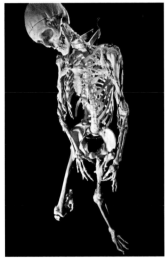

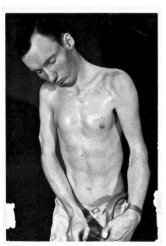

specimen – Harry Eastlack's skeleton – exemplifies how the collections speak to varied audiences. Eastlack is the only complete skeleton on display in North America that shows fibrodysplasia ossificans progressiva (FOP), a rare disease in which the connective tissue ossifies, condemning sufferers to an early death (Figure 10). Although a rare phenomenon, the key to understanding this disease is itself a key to understanding bone growth. Unusually for specimens in the museum, Eastlack's skeleton is not an anonymous specimen: it is displayed with childhood photographs of him, showing his transformation from a smiling child to a sombre adult who cannot move his limbs (Figure 11).

Frederick Kaplan MD, orthopaedic surgeon at the University of Pennsylvania School of Medicine, and Eileen Shore PhD, biologist at the same institution, regard the skeleton as an open scientific investigation. They led the team that, in 2006, identified the gene that causes FOP.[5] Eastlack's skeleton is also enlisted to help those living with FOP today. It is used to affirm their travails and has become a focus of hope within the International Fibrodysplasia Ossificans Progressiva Association.[6]

Interpretations of the skeleton are also produced as artworks. Laura Lindgren, publisher of Blast Books, has courted major photographic artists who have made images of these bones. The photographs appear in her two briskly selling books about the museum and its photographic collections.[7] When internationally renowned film artists Stephen and Timothy Quay (the Brothers Quay) learned about Eastlack and discovered that his sister, Helen, made occasional visits to her brother at the museum, they conceptualised a film meditation on the collections with Eastlack at its core. *Through the Weeping Glass: On the Consolations of Life Everlasting (Limbos and Afterbreezes from the Mütter Museum)* was funded by the Philadelphia Exhibits Initiative of the Pew Center for Arts and Heritage (Figure 12).[8] The title story of literature professor Kathleen R Sands' collection of short stories, *Boy of Bone: Twelve Stories Inspired by the Mütter*

FIGURE 12
The Brothers Quay film, *Through
the Weeping Glass* (2012).
Brothers Quay.

Museum (Siman Media Works, New York, 2012) is based on
Eastlack's experiences. Her youthful FOP protagonist copes
with his private terror through a gift from his physician, a Zuni
fetish carving of a dancing bear. Sands poses many what-ifs in
her exploration of the pathological sublime (Figure 13).[9]

WHAT NEXT?

The Mütter has moved vigorously to renovate its more
superannuated displays and create a new online presence
through its website. Further, to reckon with the new reality of
electronic access and research, the college now promotes it
collections and programmes for (related) medical and humanities
purposes to help court new audiences and situate itself within
broader intellectual territories. For instance, with major funding
from pharmaceutical companies, the college created *History of
Vaccines*, an interactive web-based timeline, which examines the
history of vaccines against smallpox, diphtheria, yellow fever,
and other diseases. The website links both to museum and
library collections.[10] *History of Vaccines* shows how the college
aims to use medical history to inform public health. Events at the
Mütter Museum are also followed via social media including the
museum's popular YouTube programs, *What's on the Curator's
Desk*, *The Mütter Minute* and *No Bones About It*.

FIGURE 13 (RIGHT)
Illustration for title story of *Boy of
Bone* by Kathleen R Sands (2012).
Jon Lezinsky, Siman Media Works.

Like several other similar institutions, including the Royal College of Physicians in London, the Mütter has an outdoor exhibit: an upgraded Benjamin Rush Medicinal Plant Garden with a colourful brochure and an audio tour. The garden presentation highlights early herbals in the library collection and relates to the apothecary items in the museum (Figure 14).

Every museum identifies and cultivates its audiences, anticipating visitors' wants and needs. The college's new use of 'medical humanities' to describe its collections and programmes resonates with other Philadelphia museums reaching out to the large and growing visiting public. Philadelphia's medical world no longer needs the college and its collections for professional development and advancement. Rather, the college is partially sustained by an exuberant museum as a cultural fixture determined to place the medical humanities within Philadelphia's intellectual history. Although the Mütter respects approaches within the sciences and arts, it is not bashful about parodying itself to show that the business of being human mixes the sublime and the farcical. For an April Fool's joke, the museum issued a press release that it now holds the world copyright on the umlaut. Such playfulness perhaps reduces visitors' anxiety in contemplating their own mortality through a museum visit while they still have a before, and an after, and a when.

FIGURE 14
Arial view of the Benjamin Rush
Medicinal Plant Garden in 2011.
Evi Numen, The College of
Physicians of Philadelphia.

NOTES

1. Jorge Luis Borges, 'The Enigmas', in *Selected Poems*, ed. by Alexander Coleman (New York: Penguin Books, 1999), p. 215.

2. Whitfield J Bell, Jr, *The College of Physicians of Philadelphia: A Bicentennial History* (Canton, Mass.: Science History Publications, 1987).

3. *The Medical News and Library*, 17 (February, 1859), 30.

4. Ella N Wade, 'A Curator's Story of the Mütter Museum and College Collections', *Transactions & Studies of The College of Physicians of Philadelphia*, 4th series, 42 (1974), 170–71.

5. Jennifer Couzin, 'Bone Disease Gene Finally Found', *Science*, 28 April, 312 (2006), 514–15; Frederick S. Kaplan, 'Fibrodysplasia Ossificans Progressiva: An Historical Perspective', *Clinical Reviews in Bone and Mineral Metabolism*, 3 (2005), 179–181.

6. 'FOP Skeleton Continues to Reveal Clues Following Gene Discovery', *FOP Connection*, 21 (2008), 13.

7. Gretchen Worden, *Mütter Museum of the College of Physicians of Philadelphia* (New York: Blast Books, 2002); *Mütter Museum Historic Medical Photographs*, ed. by Laura Lindgren (New York: Blast Books, 2007).

8. Robert D Hicks, 'The Image that Shocks the Camera', essay insert, in *Quay Brothers, Through the Weeping Glass: On the Consolations of Life Everlasting* (Limbos & Afterbreezes in the Mütter Museum) (Philadelphia: The College of Physicians of Philadelphia, 2011, on DVD); The Pew Center for Arts and Heritage, 'Center Spotlight: September 2011', www.pcah.us/the-center/newsroom/center-spotlight-september-2011.

9. M Dery, 'A Young Person's Guide to the Pathological Sublime', http://boingboing.net/2009/08/04/a-young-persons-guid.html.

10. *History of Vaccines* website, www.historyofvaccines.org.

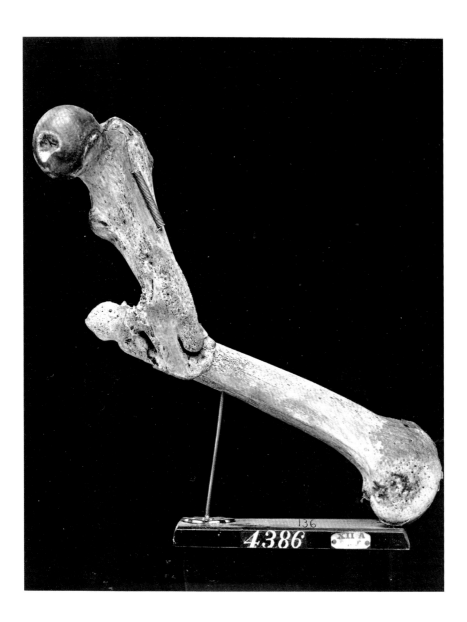

FIGURE 1
Private George Lemon was injured 5
May 1864; he survived an amputation
at the hip joint, and his ill-knit
femur was placed in the museum.
National Museum of Health and Medicine.

An army museum or a national collection?

Shifting interests and fortunes at the National Museum of Health and Medicine

Michael Rhode

For 150 years there has been a medical museum in Washington, DC. It was founded by the army during the American Civil War to undertake research and produce medical books. After the war it expanded to include wider aspects of medicine and surgery, and even attempted worldwide coverage during the late nineteenth century. Changes in medical knowledge prompted a focus on pathology, which became its primary role for most of the twentieth century; nevertheless, it has operated throughout its history at the intersection of military and civilian medicine. Even though the museum is national in terms of the scope of its collection, its roots in the army mean that it sits outside the umbrella of the Smithsonian Institution (see Chelnick in this volume).

The Army Medical Museum was born of practical medical necessities, designed to be a national institution, and run by the federal government for the benefit of its citizens. Shortly after war broke out in 1861, Surgeon General William Hammond established it in Washington, DC, and it was founded in May the following year as the nation's first federal medical research institute. Hammond based it on collections of anatomical specimens to investigate the treatment of disease and injuries

FIGURE 2
Civil War US Army Surgeon
General's Office's Officers in 1864.
Surgeon General Joseph K Barnes
is standing third from left. Assistant
Surgeon George A Otis (Curator,
Army Medical Museum) is seated
at the far left, facing Assistant
Surgeons John S Billings and Joseph
J Woodward at the far right.
National Museum of Health and Medicine.

in soldiers but it soon exhibited objects as well. The museum functioned as a reference collection displayed in open storage so that groups of gunshot-damaged bones, for instance, arranged according to the part of the body they came from, filled the shelves like books sharing a theme. Specimen-labelling was minimal – written to be understood by doctors who also relied on printed catalogues – and exhibits were not overlaid with a written narrative. For example, fractured skulls would be displayed together in a case, but labels explaining the differences in fractures or the treatment of them were not deemed necessary. While the museum soon opened to the public, the concept of explaining the objects to non-specialist viewers would take decades for the museum's curators to adopt.

The collections were primarily created to produce the six-volume *Medical and Surgical History of the War of the Rebellion*.[1] This project defined the museum's public and professional role for almost two decades. Three army surgeons (John Hill Brinton, JJ Woodward and later George Otis) acted as curators, compiling the types of injuries and diseases a military doctor could expect to treat. The specimens collected for *Medical and Surgical History* – whether shattered bones or diseased organs – were catalogued, studied and displayed (Figure 1). The books purchased in support of this research formed the foundation for the National Library of Medicine.

The museum's first home was John Hill Brinton's room in the Surgeon General's Office in a non-descript office building near the White House. On 1 August 1862, General Hammond ordered Brinton to round up specimens saved in military hospitals by surgeons for their own use. Brinton wrote to doctors throughout the country asking them to send specimens to the new museum, while promising them credit in the catalogue. He also travelled to battlefields, meeting surgeons and collecting specimens. Hearing of a battle near Washington, he would ride out and assist in the surgery and, at the same time, show the surgeons what he was seeking. He did not stop there, however. 'Many and many a putrid heap [of amputated limbs] have I had dug out of trenches where they had been buried', he recalled.[2] After the bones were removed, they were sent to the museum where they were cleaned and mounted for study.

George Otis replaced Brinton as head of the museum and curator of the surgical section in 1864, while JJ Woodward remained as curator of the medical and microscopical section (Figure 2). By 1866, less than a year after the war's conclusion, the museum had expanded the scope of its collecting to 'embrace the whole field of pathology.'[3] The growing museum moved three times in its first two years to office spaces in downtown Washington but, after President Lincoln's assassination there in 1865, the federal government purchased and renovated the notorious Ford's Theatre (the site of the shooting) to house the museum and the Surgeon General's Library. The move, beginning in December 1866, permitted the museum to

FIGURE 3
The museum's display space on the top floor of the former Ford's Theatre in the late 1860s.
National Museum of Health and Medicine.

expand its collecting to include Native American weapons and 'specimens of comparative anatomy.'[4] Congress supported the new museum, providing $5,000 a year to run it. With larger exhibit space and broader scope, it became a well-known Washington-area landmark. It even featured in Dr S Weir Mitchell's 1866 *Atlantic Monthly* story, 'The Case of George Dedlow', in which the hero was contacted during a séance by spirits of his amputated legs communing with him from their museum home.[5]

   The museum had no difficulty attracting the public. Medical specimens, including many anomalies and curiosities, fascinated lay and professional visitors alike. Part of the fascination lay in the curiosity stimulated by the prospect of seeing human remains. A reporter for the popular *Appleton's Journal* captured the atmosphere, noting 'it is, indeed, not such a collection as the timid would care to visit at midnight, and alone. Fancy the pale moonlight lighting up with a blueish tinge, the blanched skeletons and grinning skulls – the same moon that saw, in many a case, the death-blow given, or the bullet pierce.'[6] In the aftermath of the Civil War the displays of specimens from maimed soldiers of both sides led visitors to also see the museum as an unintentional national memorial (Figure 3).

FIGURE 4 (LEFT)
'The Main Hall of the Army Medical Museum—Washington' engraving from Mary Ames' 1871 guidebook. National Museum of Health and Medicine.

FIGURE 5 (RIGHT)
John Shaw Billings, head of the Army Medical Museum and Library, probably around 1870. (National Library of Medicine portrait no. 5.) National Library of Medicine.

THE MAIN HALL OF THE ARMY MEDICAL MUSEUM. — WASHINGTON.

FIGURE 6
Architect Adolph Cluss' 1885
drawing of the building to
replace Ford's Theatre.
National Museum of Health and Medicine.

By the end of 1867 (eight months after opening) the museum had drawn around 6,000 visitors (Figure 4). 'It cannot fail to be one of the most absorbing spots on earth to the student of surgery or medicine,' opined guidebook author Mary Ames in 1874, 'but to the unscientific mind, especially to one still aching with the memories of war, it must remain a museum of horrors. [...] No! the Museum is very interesting, but can never be a popular place to visit.'[7] Nevertheless, by 1874 the monthly number of visitors sometimes reached more than 2,600, even though it was only open five hours on weekdays, and four on Saturday.

After Otis's and Woodward's deaths in the early 1880s, Surgeon General's Office librarian John Shaw Billings was the man most determined to transform the Army Medical Museum into a National Medical Museum (Figure 5). Billings is best known today as the founder of the National Library of Medicine, but in 1883 Surgeon General Joseph Barnes placed him in charge of the newly merged Army Medical Museum and Library. Billings began expanding the museum's collections with the vision and energy he had brought to building the library's holdings. In addition to collecting, Billings exhibited more objects and compiled new catalogues. By this time, Civil War research was

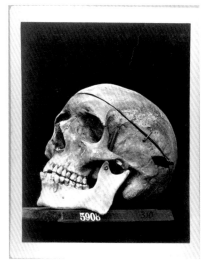

FIGURE 7
Cranium with an iron arrowhead
impacted in the left temporal
bone. The original caption reads
in part, 'Private Martin W_____,
Troop E, 4th Cavalry, was killed
by Indians on September 30, 1870,
twenty miles from Fort Concho,
Texas, while on duty as one of the
mail-stage guard'. The skull would
have arrived in the museum within
a month or so of his death, and
been photographed soon after.
National Museum of Health and Medicine.

winding down but other research was underway, especially in the new science of anthropology, which was seen as an outgrowth of anatomy – Otis was particularly interested in craniology and planned a grand publication on the skull collection.[8]

The Ford's Theatre building was proving inadequate for the growing museum and library collections and by the 1880s the museum attracted 40,000 visits per year. In his annual message to Congress, President Rutherford Hayes asked for money to replace the building, arguing 'the collection of books, specimens, and records constituting the Army Medical Museum and Library are of national importance [...] Their destruction would be an irreparable loss not only to the United States but to the world'.[9] Surgeon General Barnes noted that the collections had moved beyond their foundations in military medicine and now had important uses in the investigation of public health issues. After an hour of debate, Congress approved a new building on the US National Mall (Figure 6).

The move to the new home across from the Smithsonian's National Museum took months to complete. The two institutions continued to work closely together, swapping collections and advice. New space also enabled Billings to aggressively enlarge the collections. In addition to illustrating 'the effects, both immediate and remote, of wounds and of the disease that prevailed in the Army,' he looked specifically to obtain 'specimens to illustrate the methods of work of the best anatomists, physiologists and pathologists of Europe'[10] (Figure 7). He sent army doctors an extensive wish list with twenty-four categories including 'abnormities [sic]' and 'deformities'[11] (Figure 8). Billings focused on human anatomy and embryology, pathology, numismatics, ethnography and physical anthropology, comparative anatomy, specimen preparation, and the development of the microscope (Figure 9). He also collected medical instruments and military artefacts, including equipment and supplies, especially those of foreign armies. These new collections were an attempt to build a national medical museum

FIGURE 8 (RIGHT)
Two-headed calf photographed by
Ross Hall of Millersburg, Ohio, in
June 1888. In spite of requesting
'abnormities', Billings drew the line
at purchasing them; he insisted he
was not running a 'dime museum'.
National Museum of Health and Medicine.

FIGURE 9 (BELOW)
Robert Hooke's microscope, made
for him by Christopher Cock of
London after 1665, and purchased
by Billings for the museum
with his own money in 1886.
National Museum of Health and Medicine.

with a broad encyclopaedic reach for use by the nation's medical community, and interested members of the general public, while maintaining specialised medical research conducted by staff on topics such as medical photography, water safety, pathology and bacteriology.

In 1888 Billings outlined his vision of the 'National Medical Museum'. Excluding microscope slides, Billings noted that the museum held over 15,000 specimens and it was not a small, local 'anatomical museum' but a medical museum of broad scope and significance (Figure 10). Borrowing the Smithsonian's motto, the museum's mission was 'to preserve, to diffuse, and to increase knowledge', especially because 'a large proportion of the pathological specimens in this museum illustrate conditions which now rarely occur, forming a group which it is safe to say will never be duplicated'.[12]

Billings also anticipated the decline of those medical collections not affiliated with a medical school or society, noting 'a medical museum is really used, for purposes of study, by very few persons [...] American physicians [...] are not accustomed to make use of them.'[13] Museums, Billings felt, never assumed the role that libraries had in being a fundamental platform for research. However, the Army Medical Museum exhibited

FIGURE 10 (LEFT)
The Great Hall of the
museum in the 1890s.
National Museum of Health and Medicine.

FIGURE 11 (MIDDLE)
Trench foot in a bisected museum
specimen from World War I.
National Museum of Health and Medicine.

FIGURE 12 (RIGHT)
New exhibits were put in place
during World War I, including this
anatomical exhibit shown in 1920.
National Museum of Health and Medicine.

specimens at world's fairs and expositions, greatly increasing its popular audience. Woodward had been responsible for the medical department's large exhibit at the 1876 Centennial Exposition in Philadelphia, including a new hospital-style building filled with museum displays and catalogues. Billings oversaw the museum's exhibits for the Chicago World's Columbian Exposition of 1893, and wrote catalogues on the history of the microscope and on selected specimens.

Billings retired in 1895 and his successor, Walter Reed, pursued the new science of bacteriology, which – along with the x-ray – seemed in some contexts to threaten with obsolescence the concept of a medical museum as a place to study whole specimens mounted in jars of alcohol. Now much medical research was conducted through the microscope or in a laboratory. However, the focus on research at the Army Medical Museum actually increased under Reed and his successors, who discovered mosquitoes carried yellow fever and designed a typhoid fever vaccine. Although the museum was still a popular public attraction, in 1893 the Army Medical School had opened in the museum's space and shared its staff; as a consequence the space allocated to public exhibitions diminished. And although

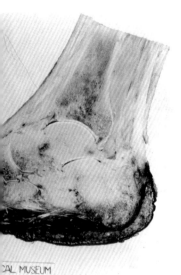

only the 'pick of the collections' remained on display, by 1913 the remaining exhibit space nonetheless unfortunately became 'much overcrowded.'[14]

With World War I the museum was firmly on the road to becoming a pathological institute focusing on research and education for the medical profession; thousands of specimens were collected from the field, diseases such as gas gangrene and trench foot were diagnosed, and *The Medical Department of the United States Army in the World War* was published (Figure 11).[15] Responses to the war in the museum also reinvigorated exhibitions with new displays of wartime hazards such as shell shock and new divisions for motion pictures and photography. But, as a result of changes in medical education, the rise of laboratory medicine, and especially the growth of specialisation in medicine, the museum's previous roles and relevance – and thus the collecting of bottled 'wet tissues' and historical medical technologies – diminished (Figure 12).

World War II confirmed the museum's primary role in pathological consultation, as specimens of diseases never seen in North America flowed in from around the world and staff sent back diagnoses and recommendations. During the war all of the exhibit space except for the main exhibit hall was converted to offices for military use. Yet despite this and wartime travel restrictions, 200,000 people still visited annually. Still, wartime curator and pathologist James Ash did not regard public display as the organisation's central function, noting that 'we still suffer under the connotation 'museum', an institution still thought of by many as a repository for bottled monsters and medical curiosities. To be sure, we have such specimens. As is required by law, we maintain an exhibit open to the public, but in war time, at least, the museum per se is the least of our functions'.[16] In fact the museum became a small division of the Army Institute of Pathology in 1946 that, three years later, formed the Armed Forces Institute of Pathology (AFIP). The museum was thus named the Medical Museum of the AFIP and subsequently the Armed Forces Medical Museum.

However, as the institute grew, the museum was frequently shunted aside. In 1947 the entire museum moved across the street into a temporary building known as Chase Hall and was reorganised into separate public and professional museums (Figure 13). The professional museum consisted of the large majority of the preserved human tissue collections, simply placed in a space according to their location in the body

FIGURE 13 (BELOW, LEFT)
In the 1950s and early 1960s, the museum's exhibits were just off the Mall in a temporary building known as Chase Hall.
National Museum of Health and Medicine.

FIGURE 14 (BELOW, RIGHT)
The National Historic Landmark status was transferred from the museum building to the collection around 1968 when the Hirschhorn Museum replaced it on the Mall.
National Museum of Health and Medicine.

section but without any attempt to arrange them as an exhibit. The museum open to the general public, including tourists, featured historical collections, exhibits on then-current medical topics, and 'contributions to medicine by the Army.'[17] By 1954, public exhibits remained downtown while a new atomic-bomb-proof building for the pathological institute opened five miles away at Walter Reed Army Medical Center (WRAMC), where the 'professional' museum existed for study and research by government and civilian physicians.

In the 1950s, the public museum presented focused medical exhibitions – originally created for the institute's scientists and their professional meetings – such as *Distinctive Tumors of the World*, *Round Worm Infections* and *Urologic Antiquities* but these nevertheless remained popular with lay visitors. Indeed, curator Samuel Kime noted in 1956 that the museum was the only collection of actual pathological specimens accessible to the general public in the United States.[18] After the library decamped in 1962, the public museum returned to the building erected on the Mall in 1888 and two years later it was declared a National Historic Landmark. In 1966 the museum had 765,157 visitors but, that same year, Joseph Hirshhorn donated his art collection to the nation. Congress chose to house Hirshhorn's collection on the site where the 'public' museum stood. In a novel interpretation, the landmark status awarded to the building was transferred to the medical museum's collections it used to house (Figure 14).

Closing in 1968, by 1971 it reopened at WRAMC, far from Washington's downtown, only to reclose in 1974 for four years while its space housed a military medical school (Figure 15). While the Smithsonian's audience grew immensely in the following decades, the museum's attendance did not. In 1988 the museum was reinvigorated and renamed the National Museum of Health and Medicine (Figure 16) but the location on a military base limited public accessibility. When WRAMC closed in 2011, the museum moved again to another army base at an industrial park in a suburban neighborhood of Silver Spring, Maryland. On 21

May it reopened to the public on its 150th anniversary – for the first time not even in the nation's capital. With this last move, exhibition space was reduced from about 15,000ft² to a third of that, and storage space for the collection was also smaller, but at least visitor attendance has remained constant.

The museum has survived 150 years during which time it has undergone numerous name changes and relocations – including to office buildings, a converted theatre, a specially designed building on the Mall, temporary spaces in wartime, a medical centre and now to the suburbs. With these shifts have come irreparable losses to some of the collections. Yet for over a century a non-professional audience has continued to show interest in its displays of medicine and the dead. Visitors are now largely school groups or people on bus tours of America. However, its current location makes it difficult for a casual visitor to find. Furthermore, there is no space for the expansion of exhibits or storage. So, presently, it seems that the museum's audience numbers will never remotely rival those of institutions, such as the American History Museum, which attracts 4.5 million per year. These spatial restrictions are likely to continue for the forty years of the new building's lifespan but at least the museum was not closed and dissolved as the pathology institute was – perhaps because of its continuing capacity to attract public interest. Even as healthcare costs surge and medical research promises dramatic new improvements for human health, the museum appears destined to remain a minor footnote in military medicine, unused by the majority of the citizens who support it through their taxes – much as Billings had predicted in 1888.

FIGURE 15 (ABOVE)
Constructing the new
museum wing in 1970.
National Museum of Health and Medicine.

NOTES

1. United States Army Surgeon General's Office, *The Medical and Surgical History of the War of the Rebellion*, 6 vols (Washington: US Government Printing Office, 1870–88).

2. John Hill Brinton, *Personal Memoirs of John H. Brinton, Civil War Surgeon, 1861–1865* (Carbondale: Southern Illinois University Press, 1996), p. 187.

3. Otis to Cook, 24 March 1866, Curatorial Records: Letter Books of the Curators, 1863 1910, Otis Historical Archives, National Museum of Health and Medicine (OHA).

4. Otis to William Forwood, 4 January 1867, OHA.

5. Anonymous [S. Weir Mitchell], 'The Case of George Dedlow,' *Atlantic Monthly*, 18:105 (July 1866), 1–11. For a modern interpretation of Mitchell's work, see Robert Goler, 'Loss and the Persistence of Memory: "The Case of George Dedlow" and Disabled Civil War Veterans,' *Literature and Medicine*, 23 (2004), 160–83.

6. Louis Bagger, 'The Army Medical Museum in Washington', *Appleton's Journal*, 1 March 1873, 294–97.

7. Mary Clemmer Ames, *Ten Years in Washington: Life and Scenes in the National Capital as a Woman Sees Them* (Hartford, CT: Worthington, 1874), p. 477.

8. Daniel S Lamb, 'A History of the United States Army Medical Museum 1862 to 1917 Compiled from the Official Records,' unpublished typescript, 1917, OHA.

9. Robert S Henry, *The Armed Forces Institute of Pathology: Its First Century 1862–1962* (Washington: Office of the Surgeon General, 1964), p. 74.

10. Billings to E C Carter, 19 November 1886, OHA.

11. Lamb, 'A History', pp. 96–101.

12. John Shaw Billings, 'Medical Museums, with Special Reference to the Army Medical Museum at Washington', *Medical News*, 22 September 1888, p. 314.

13. Billings, 'Medical Museums', p. 314.

14. McCaw to Surgeon General's Office, 21 November 1913, quoted in Henry, *The Armed Forces Institute of Pathology*, 150–51.

15. *The Medical Department of the United States Army in the World War*, ed. By Charles Lynch et al., 15 vols (Washington, DC: US Government Printing Office, 1921–29).

16. JE Ash, 'The Army Medical Museum in This War,' *Southern Medical Journal*, 37:5 (May 1944), 261–66.

17. Armed Forces Institute of Pathology, *Annual Report* (Washington, DC: AFIP, 1947), p. 22.

18. Samuel Kime, 'John Q Public, Glass, Plastic, and Our Specimens,' *AFIP Letter*, 31 July 1956.

FIGURE 16 (BELOW)
The facial reconstruction section in *Battlefield Surgery 101*, around 2010. National Museum of Health and Medicine. Photograph by Kathleen Stocker.

Collecting medical technology

at the Smithsonian Institution's National Museum of American History

Judy M Chelnick

Artefacts from across the United States and beyond – from individuals and corporations – routinely find their way into the medical collection of the Smithsonian Institution, within the largest museum complex in the world. Like the Science Museum in London (see Bud in this volume), the Smithsonian's medical collection resides within a larger museum – the National Museum of American History. This is part of a vast organisation comprising nineteen museums, research centres and a zoo. The Smithsonian's medical collection, while not the oldest in the United States, maintains a special distinction of being part of America's national collections. This chapter explores this collection, highlighting significant aspects, especially medical objects relating to the human heart.[1]

BEGINNINGS

The Smithsonian Institution was established in 1846. Thirty years later, the medical collection began with the acquisition of thousands of materia medica specimens (medicinal plant, mineral and animal products – Figure 1) kept from the Chinese Pavilion of America's Centennial Exposition in Philadelphia. James Flint MD USN became the first curator of this collection. With a view to expansion, Flint outlined criteria for collecting 'in

the field'. An 1881 memorandum explained how to collect and document materia medica specimens, emphasising the need to 'illustrate in the fullest possible manner the medical theories and practices of mankind in every part of the world and at all periods'.[2] He later composed the more substantial *Directions for Collecting Information and Objects Illustrating the History of Medicine*, expanding the scope of collecting to include 'surgical operations and appliances', which could be given to Smithsonian associates in the field who would send them to Washington DC for cataloguing and preserving.[3] Flint's writings on collecting shaped the direction of the medical collection for the next seventy years.

Until the mid-twentieth century collecting initiatives and exhibits were generally directed at educating Americans about good health practices with the help, for example, of dioramas of sewage disposal plants and sanitary milk houses. Other more biologically oriented exhibitions explained how the body functioned, with exhibits such as *Watch Your Teeth*, which opened in 1926 (Figure 2). Rows of artefacts, like the dental patent models acquired about 1925, had a linear approach to history and

FIGURE 2 (LEFT)
Watch Your Teeth, around 1935. Many exhibits explained to visitors how to maintain a healthy body. Courtesy of the National Museum of American History, Smithsonian Institution.

FIGURE 3 (MIDDLE)
Dental patent models: the Smithsonian Institution Patent Model Collection was acquired in 1908–26, when the United States Patent Office no longer had the room or interest to showcase the collection. Courtesy of the National Museum of American History, Smithsonian Institution.

FIGURE 4 (RIGHT)
Hall of Health in the National Museum (now the Arts and Industries Building), 1957. Courtesy of the National Museum of American History, Smithsonian Institution.

FIGURE 5
Charles Lindbergh-Alexis Carrell
perfusion pumps, around 1938.
Photograph by Richard Strauss. Courtesy
of the National Museum of American
History, Smithsonian Institution.

meagre descriptive labels were a typical exhibition technique (Figure 3). The early 1960s saw the renovation of the Health Hall with the Transparent Woman as its centerpiece. Standing on an elevated platform, the German model systematically explained how the body's organs work (Figure 4).

Although Flint had intended to build a comprehensive medical collection including instruments, his priorities and those of his immediate successors were the materia medica and pharmaceuticals. Otherwise, the earliest acquisitions included a rabbit foot, human hair, bloodletting and cupping apparatus, and a cautery iron. Eventually the collection would expand to include objects representing pharmacy, dentistry and public health.

INSTRUMENTS OF THE HEART

Before World War II most of the collection's medical equipment was nineteenth and early twentieth-century surgical apparatus. At mid-century there was an increased interest in contemporary medical instrumentation of all kinds, and the two full-time curators were concerned with pharmacy, public health, medicine and dentistry. Curator John Blake (in post 1957 to 1961) added many significant artefacts to the collection, including a nineteenth-century bacteriology laboratory from the Rockefeller Institute with equipment used by pioneering research scientists Simon Flexner, Hideyo Noguchi, Jacques Loeb and Alfred Cohn.[4] Blake's most significant contribution came in 1961 when he acquired the glass pump designed by Nobel Prize winner Alexis Carrel and aviator Charles Lindbergh. Dubbed the 'artificial heart' by the popular press, the Carrel-Lindbergh perfusion pump is perhaps the most iconic artefact in the history of bionics, the precursor to the heart-lung machine introduced in the 1950s (Figure 5).

In the museum, early 1950s in-house exhibits had been put together on a shoestring budget utilising ingenuity and inexpensive materials (Figure 6).[5] Yet several major artefacts were collected for an important exhibition on the heart in 1954,

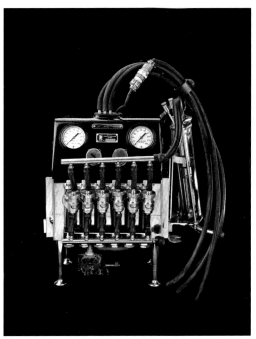

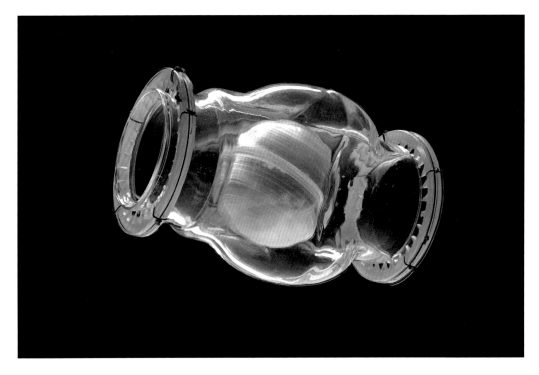

including the Dodrill-GMR Mechanical Heart developed by engineers at the General Motors Research Laboratories under the leadership of surgeon Forrest Dewey Dodrill of Harper Hospital in Detroit, Michigan (Figure 7). Used in the world's first open heart surgery in 1952, the 'Michigan heart' bypassed the right and left sides of the heart as well as the lungs. A further significant acquisition was the 1914 string galvanometer used by Frank Wilson, who had pioneered electrocardiography at the University of Michigan.

The study of heart disease in the US, from the mid-twentieth century, explored causes, risks and means of prevention, encouraged by the National Heart Institute. Advances in the mechanical manipulation of the heart were also well underway with the development of the heart-lung machine, pacemakers, artificial heart valves and arteries (Figure 8). Because of the fast-paced nature of experimental cardiac research, the Smithsonian became the beneficiary of many unique artefacts. Many of these featured in the new Hall of Medicine at the National Museum of History and Technology, which opened in 1966. The exhibition was timely: the first heart transplant was performed in the next year, followed in 1969 by the first artificial heart implantation.

Objects continued to arrive. Whether in the hope of immortality or from a keen sense of history, many famous individuals without solicitation generously donated artefacts to the national collections. Such had been the case with a prototype defibrillator developed by James Rand for his friend Claude Beck who, in 1947, successfully defibrillated the heart of a young boy, restoring its normal rhythm with an electric shock. In 1978, almost a decade following the implantation of the first total artificial heart in a human, cardiac surgeon Denton Cooley donated the historic pump developed by his colleague Domingo Liotta (Figure 9).

After implantation of the Jarvik-7 Total Artificial Heart into Barney Clark in 1982, Smithsonian curators began to collect contemporary bionic artefacts, mechanical replacement or

FIGURE 6 (TOP LEFT)
Telegram From Your Heart was part of an exhibit that coincided with the Second World Cardiology Conference held in Washington, DC, in September 1954.
Courtesy of the National Museum of American History, Smithsonian Institution.

FIGURE 7 (TOP RIGHT)
The Dodrill-GMR Mechanical Heart, 1952, was a collaborative project headed by Dr FD Dodrill of Harper Hospital and the General Motors Research Laboratories in Detroit, Michigan.
Courtesy of the National Museum of American History, Smithsonian Institution. Photograph by Richard Strauss.

FIGURE 8 (BOTTOM)
The first successful artificial heart valve developed and implanted by Dr Charles Hufnagel of Georgetown University in Washington DC, around 1950.
Courtesy of the National Museum of American History, Smithsonian Institution. Photograph by Hugh Talman.

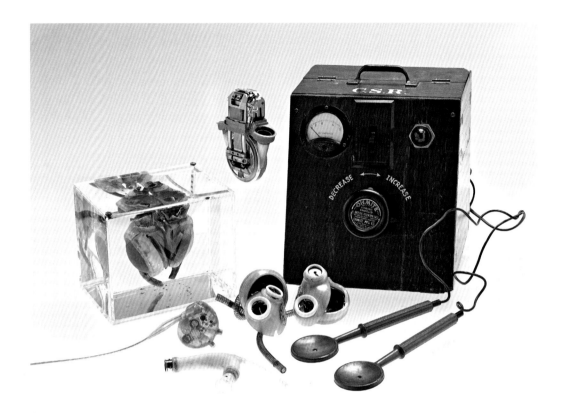

assistance devices for failing body organs or limbs. Curator Barbara Melosh (in post 1983 to 1991) actively sought to acquire a Jarvik-7 for the collection in discussion with inventor Robert Jarvik. But Jarvik's condition for donation – the permanent display of the artefact – could not be met by the museum. (As a matter of policy, museums tend not to guarantee that a donated object will be exhibited.) The Smithsonian later realised its goal when the University of Arizona donated a Jarvik-7. Melosh highlighted the importance of this object, arguing that the Jarvik-7 'exemplifies the possibilities and limitations of advanced medical technology', and that 'the artificial heart is in many ways a quintessentially American Project, dramatising the American bent for aggressive intervention and a medical economics often skewed to investment in the sophisticated treatment of acute illnesses'.[6] Melosh's probing analysis thus

FIGURE 9
Cardiology: *Clockwise from right*, Beck Defibrillator 1947; dissected Jarvik-7 Artificial Heart implanted 1985; Liotta-Hall Intracorporeal Pump 1964; Chardack-Greatbatch Pacemaker about 1961; Liotta-Cooley Artificial Heart, 1969; and the Novacor Left Ventricular Assist Device, around 1984.
Courtesy of the National Museum of American History, Smithsonian Institution. Photograph by Hugh Talman.

FIGURE 10
M*A*S*H, the Exhibit, 1983. *M*A*S*H*
is arguably the most popular exhibit
ever at the National Museum of
American History. Visitors stood in
line to see the SWAMP, the operating
room and other artefacts from
the popular television series.
Courtesy of the National Museum of
American History, Smithsonian Institution.

recognised in American medical practices the thirst for newer, bigger and 'better' technologies, as well as the professional enthusiasm that seeks a cure while sometimes leading to the premature introduction of devices and techniques.

ARTIFICIAL ORGANS

The missions of museum institutions and their collecting philosophies change to reflect contemporary goals. This was the case in 1981, when the National Museum of History and Technology was renamed the National Museum of American History. The museum's agenda became cultural rather than technological and, with regard to the medical collection, there was a new concentration almost exclusively on the history of American medicine. During this period curators throughout the museum began to modify the way that they acquired artefacts, becoming more selective in their collecting practices with greater emphasis on attaching supporting documentation to artefacts. The immersion of iconic popular culture artefacts into the museum's collections was enthusiastically endorsed by all collecting units. The medical collection contributed to this trend with the acquisition of several sets from the television show *M*A*S*H*, which was based on a fictional medical hospital during the Korean War (Figure 10).

Further, more subtle changes are also evident. Thirty years ago collecting was dominated by the curator's limited view of the physicians' medical world. Today, collecting is significantly more complex. It is not enough to collect an artefact and provide a meagre two sentence description of the object: it is necessary to enhance understanding of the object's invention process, its functions, and the dynamics between the object and its users. Of crucial interest are also relationships between

FIGURE 11
Recent acquisitions to the Paediatrics and Neonatal Intensive Care Unit Collections: *from left to right*, a Belcroy tube feeder for premature infants, about 1935; preemie (prematurely born infant) pacifier and pacifier choking test stand, about 2003; Bili-bonnet, a phototherapy mask to protect the eyes of babies being treated for jaundice, about 2003; identification bracelet for new born, 1957; and a customised helmet for the correction of plagiocephaly, 2007. Courtesy of the National Museum of American History, Smithsonian Institution. Photograph by Hugh Talman.

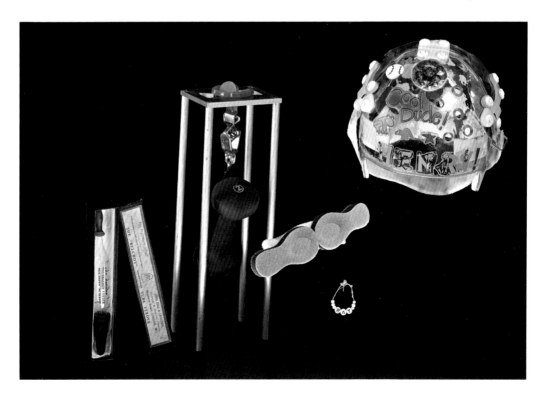

scientists and engineers in the object's initial development, the successes and consequences of its implementation and – just as importantly – patients' experiences of that object (see Edmonson in this volume).

This approach is illustrated by an initiative that ushered in a new dynamic in medical collecting: *Project Bionics*, established in 2000. As a collaborative venture – between the Smithsonian's Division of Medicine and Science, the Division of History at the National Library of Medicine and the American Society of Artificial Internal Organs – the project aims to preserve the history of artificial organs.

The project's first collecting achievement is the Kolff Collection. Willem J Kolff was the inventor of the first successful artificial kidney, and it was in his laboratory that the Jarvik-7 Total Artificial Heart was developed. Kolff's collection of artificial kidneys and hearts, ventricular assist devices, ceramic moulds of human and animal organs, and numerous drive units, represents Kolff's legacy as the 'father of artificial organs'. It also illustrates the false steps and protracted successes scientists have undertaken to heal defective human hearts. It speaks to the trial and error of new designs and materials as well as the occasionally combative relations between physicians and engineers.

PATIENTS' AND INVENTORS' VIEWS

Contemporary collecting has expanded to include patients' perspectives on illness. Objects in the medical collection closely linked to patients and their quality of life include, for example, wigs and prosthetics from breast cancer patients, and a fly-fishing vest cut and modified to accommodate the attachments necessary for an AbioCor® electrohydraulic artificial heart to function. A custom-made paediatric helmet for plagiocephaly (unusual skull flattening) is a recent acquisition. The helmet's accession file includes an account of the child's and parent's experiences during the five months the helmet was worn to

FIGURE 12
The newly installed Holter
Monitor (about 1971) with other
medical objects including Yorick,
a plastic skeleton embedded
with bionics from head to toe.
Courtesy of the National Museum of
American History, Smithsonian Institution.
Photograph by Richard Strauss.

correct severe asymmetry. The donor, the baby's mother, details the entire procedure from the initial diagnosis through to the process of cutting the child's hair before a plaster mould of his head could be made, and on to the weekly adjustments that gradually reshaped his head. As the helmet was decorated with the child's name, Henry, this is not simply an anonymous medical artefact, for it visibly bears the trace of a person (Figure 11).

The Small Beginnings® donation was another significant project contributing to both the museum's medical collection and its Lemelson Center for the History of Invention and Innovation, founded in 1995. Within this project a curator, historian and archivist documented women's roles in medicine and their contribution to invention and technology in healthcare. The first goal was to collect artefacts and archival materials from Sharon Rogone, inventor and entrepreneur. Rogone's experience of the lack of appropriately sized medical equipment in the early days of a Californian neonatal intensive care unit inspired her to develop and patent a phototherapy mask for premature infants to wear over their eyes during jaundice treatment. Like many donors before her, she agreed to sit down to an interview as part of the documentation process.

The foreseeable future of medical collecting at the Smithsonian aims to document and display developments from the initial emergence of an object through to its use by patients. And it aims to conduct this collecting in a consultative and collaborative way, using appropriate technologies. While collecting, medical curators are mindful of the multiplicity of constituencies served: visitors to the museum, whether local, national or international; students, researchers and healthcare workers. Audiences have expanded through our presence on the web, the *Smithsonian Magazine* and the new Smithsonian television channel. The goal is to attract and engage as wide an audience as possible: not all visitors are physicians but at some point all are patients (Figure 12).

NOTES

1. Judy M Chelnick, 'From Stethoscopes to Artificial Hearts: 150 Years of Collecting Medical History at the Smithsonian Institution', *Caduceus*, 13/3 (1997), 1–69. Other major collections include imaging and biotechnology. See Ramunas Kondratas 'Medical Imaging' and Patricia Peck Gossel, 'Laboratory Apparatus' in '150 Years of Collecting Medical History at the Smithsonian Institution', *Caduceus*, 13/3 (1997) 1–69.

2. James M Flint, 'Memoranda for Collectors of Drugs for the Materia Medica Section of the National Museum', *Proceedings of the United States National Museum*, 4 (1881), appendix 8.

3. James M Flint, 'Directions for Collecting Information and Objects Illustrating the History of Medicine', *Bulletin of the United States National Museum*, 39 (1905), part S.

4. Letters of John Blake to Anthony J Campo, superintendent of Purchases, The Rockefeller Institute, Accession File 224610.

5. George Griffinhagen, interview by Judy M Chelnick, 14 June 2012.

6. Barbara Melosh to the Collections Committee, Washington, DC, National Museum of American History, Accession File 1987.0474.01.

Morbid anatomy

Joanna Ebenstein

Morbid Anatomy is a project that explores the overlaps between art and medicine via words and images, art and scholarship, in both the virtual and physical world. At its core are my own photographs of wax anatomical models and specimens fashioned from actual human bodies, many of which can seem quite bizarre or even disturbing to the contemporary eye. The project reflects my interest in approaching these artefacts as artworks that express or evoke ideas about the body, disease and death. I seek to understand this material culture of medicine in the context of a long tradition of artistic and cultural responses to the certainty of death, some items of which still act as *memento mori* – objects whose very function is to remind us that we, too, will die.

For the past five years, my fascination with what might seem curious and perplexing artefacts has taken me all over the world, seeking out and photographing the museums and other spaces that house them, public and private, front of house and behind the scenes. These photographs provide the source material for exhibitions and lectures, as well as reportage. I attempt to communicate the uncanny beauty and the secret lives of these objects, which often cut across seemingly distinct domains of death and beauty, art and science, spectacle and pedagogy. Many of these anatomical artefacts were originally designed as much to incite the curiosity of a non-specialist audience as to teach medical students, such as Clemente Susini's famous eighteenth-century anatomical Venuses (see Maerker in this volume). Continuing this tradition, *Morbid Anatomy*'s aim is to present deliberately seductive images that draw viewers into encounters with the fascinating history of medicine. Its audience includes museum curators, scholars, artists, collectors and those interested in forgotten or overlooked histories.

Morbid Anatomy began as a blog, a satellite project to my 2007 exhibition *Anatomical Theatre*, which featured my photographs of artefacts in selected European and American anatomical and medical museums.[1] Soon after, I opened the Morbid Anatomy Library, a research library and private museum in Brooklyn, New York, which makes available my personal collection of books, artworks, artefacts and curiosities related to the history of art and medicine, death and culture. A recently introduced strand of the project is 'Morbid Anatomy Presents', a series of public events, including lectures by medical museum curators, private collectors, scholars and autodidacts, and an annual symposium, organised with the Coney Island Museum. For the artistically inclined, the Morbid Anatomy Art Academy offers classes in arcane and anatomically themed arts and crafts.[2]

Morbid Anatomy began as a process-based art project, a way to digitally organise my own research, as well as the visual and reference material I gathered while developing the *Anatomical Theatre* exhibition. It has since grown in surprising ways. It is unclear how it will develop in the future, especially given the rapid pace of change in digital media, but I anticipate that the audience for this material will continue to broaden as more people are drawn into the intriguing world of medical museums and their often mysterious, uncanny, and deeply compelling artefacts.

NOTES

1. Morbid Anatomy blog is at http://morbidanatomy.blogspot.com, where you can find information about visiting the Morbid Anatomy Library.
2. The Coney Island Museum is located in Brooklyn, New York; you can find out more at www.coneyisland.com/museum.shtml.

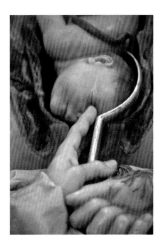

18th-century obstetrical wax
model, from the workshop of
Clemente Susini in Florence.
Now at the Josephinum, Department
and Collections of History of Medicine,
Medical University of Vienna.
Photograph by Joanna Ebenstein.

Skeleton and hand models for *la
médecine opératoire* (operative
medicine). From the Musée
Orfila (closed 2009), Paris.
Photograph by Joanna Ebenstein,
courtesy Université Paris Descartes.

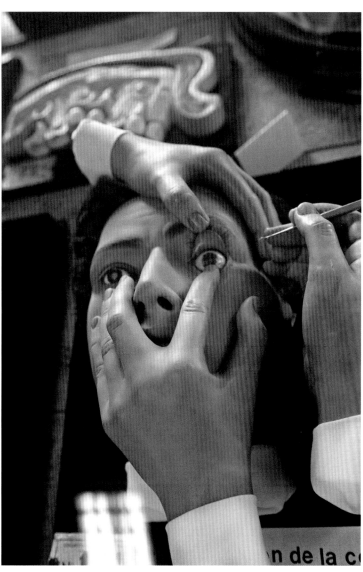

Surgery on the left eye, 19th century.
A surgical 'model in wax with the head
of the patient and three hands of the
curators' from the Spitzner collection,
Musée Orfila (closed 2009), Paris.
Photograph by Joanna Ebenstein,
courtesy Université Paris Descartes.

Victorian moulages of the hand
by Joseph Towne in the Gordon
Museum, Guys' Hospital.
Photograph by Joanna Ebenstein.

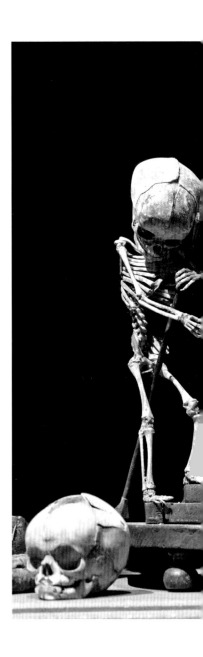

Tableau with a mummified child and
three foetal skeletons, unknown
artist, late 17th century. Now at
Galerie d'Anatomie, Ecole nationale
supérieure des Beaux-Arts de Paris.
Photograph by Joanna Ebenstein.

Display including a preparation
that demonstrates the skin
disease congenital ichthyosiform
erythroderma. Installed in the
Federal Pathologic-Anatomical
Museum (Pathologisch-anatomisches
Bundesmuseum, previously the
Narrenturm) Vienna, Austria.
Photograph by Joanna Ebenstein.

19th-century preparation
of a skeleton in the Federal
Pathologic-Anatomical Museum
(Pathologisch-anatomisches
Bundesmuseum, previously the
Narrenturm) Vienna, Austria.
Photograph by Joanna Ebenstein.

Wax on bone anatomical sculptures
by Ercole Lelli, commissioned by
Pope Benedict XIV in the 18th century,
Palazzo Poggi, Bologna, Italy.
Photograph by Joanna Ebenstein.

Plaster cast of hydrocephalus (water
on the brain), probably around 1900.
Photograph by Joanna Ebenstein,
courtesy of Museum Vrolik, Amsterdam.

Plaster models in the pathological
cabinet, the Museum of the Faculty
of Medicine at the Jagiellonian
University, Krakow, Poland.
Photograph by Joanna Ebenstein,
courtesy of the Museum of the Faculty of
Medicine at the Jagiellonian University.

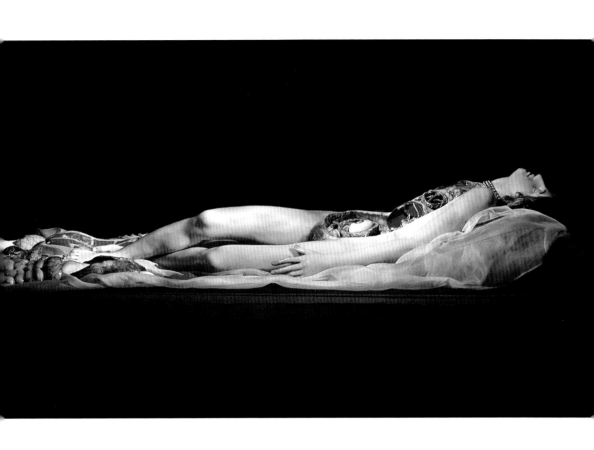

The *Venerina* or 'Little Venus'
anatomical model by Clemente Susini,
1782. Palazzo Poggi, Bologna, Italy.
Photograph by Joanna Ebenstein.

Wax anatomical study of the head,
neck and upper chest by Joseph
Towne, mid-19th century. Gordon
Museum, Guys' Hospital, London.
Photograph by Joanna Ebenstein.

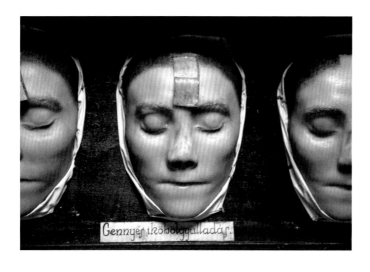

Moulage presenting phases of the
sphinoid sinus operation, attributed to
'Magyar, 1926'. From the collections
of the Semmelweis Museum,
Library and Archives of the History
of Medicine, Budapest, Hungary.
Photograph by Joanna Ebenstein.

The Morbid Anatomy Library, 2011.
Photograph by Shannon Taggart.

Afterword

Wellcome Collection and the post-medical museum?

Ken Arnold and Simon Chaplin

The medical museum is dead. Long live the medical museum.

Or rather, long live those spaces that seek to engage audiences in discussion or reflection on themes of health and wellbeing, of morbidity and mortality, of the practices of healing. And long live those that do so by using material culture, the objects that shape, or are shaped by, our understanding of what it is to be human in sickness and in health. Medical, but not overly defined by medicine. Museums, but not determined simply by their role as custodians of the accumulated material culture of medical science. With regard to the 'post-medical' museum, we envisage the emergence of institutions that seek to redefine both what is meant by 'medical' and the experience of visiting a 'museum'; and we wonder if Wellcome Collection (Figure 1) has already begun this process of redefinition.

FIGURE 1
Artist George Nuku and Maori display case in the *Skin* exhibition at Wellcome Collection, 2010.
Image: Wellcome Library, London.

This afterword discusses some aspects of this post-medical museum – especially with reference to Wellcome Collection, on London's Euston Road – after briefly reflecting on the chapters in this volume. Contemplating the future of medical museums necessarily involves appreciation of their history. Medical specimens, practitioners and institutions were, after all, significantly involved in the very earliest Renaissance wonder cabinets, and in the construction of the first 'modern' museums in the Enlightenment (see, for example, Maerker in this volume). As the preceding essays demonstrate, subsequent 'medical' museums have taken many forms. Two particular genres stand out. The first is that created specifically for the purpose of teaching and/or research, using models, specimens, casts and other artefacts as a means of communicating medical or scientific knowledge to aspirant practitioners or to the public, or as spaces in which the preserved fabric of human or animal bodies provides raw material for investigation and analysis. The second is the museum that acts as repository for, and presents the narrative of, the history of medical disciplines, of the individual medical practitioner or of the medical body corporate. These are not discrete categories. There is, often in the absence of conscious management, an elision between the first and the second, the inexorable shift from the contemporary to the historical with the passage of time. The preserved human and animal body parts assembled by John Hunter in the eighteenth century or Rudolf Virchow in the nineteenth are no longer actively used for training surgeons or pathologists: instead, they now serve as evidence for a practice that has largely (though not wholly and maybe not permanently) waned in significance in the medical curriculum (see Alberti, and Schnalke, in this volume).

The transition from one model of use to another is neither simple nor one-way. For every thriving Hunterian or Mütter Museum or Surgeons' Hall there are many more specimen collections that have not survived the decline of gross anatomy and pathology as research disciplines (see Åhrén in this volume), or whose future direction is as yet unclear (see Rhode in this volume). Elsewhere, the desire to maintain specimens as useful objects for teaching has often resulted in significant interventions. These may be physical, such as remounting, re-dissecting, even substitution; or semantic, as with relabelling, re-diagnosis and reclassification, for example (see Hallam in

FIGURE 2
Henry Wellcome with the Sultans of
Socota at an archaeological site at
Jebel Moya, Sudan, around 1913.
Image: Wellcome Library, London.

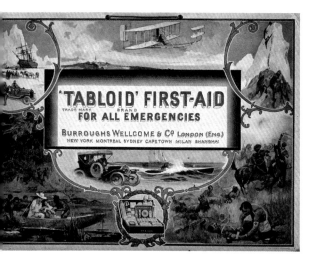

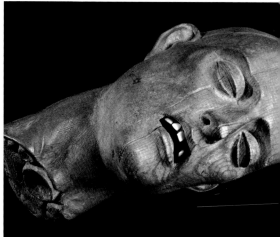

FIGURE 3 (LEFT)
Tabloid First Aid advert, around 1910.
Image: Wellcome Library, London.

FIGURE 4 (RIGHT)
Carved wooden head of a
Christian martyr, probably
French, 16th century.
Image: Wellcome Library, London.

this volume). All alter the historical character of the original object, something as true for the nineteenth century as it is today (see Hendriksen, Huistra and Knoeff in this volume).

The history of medical museums as sites for the production of medical history is similarly complex. In the Western tradition at least, medicine has been remarkably tied to its history since antiquity – with medical practitioners active in compiling and using historical narratives to advance their claims to status – and in its use of material culture in shaping disciplinary identity, as the Museum of Medical History in Zurich and the Dittrick in Cleveland illustrate (see Condrau, and Bud, in this volume). Historical collections continue to be valued for their capacity to foster, if not necessarily the specific skills of medical practice, then the sense of corporate identity that helps bind communities of practitioners together. They are also testimony to the continuing role of physical exposition as a means of exploring the history of medicine in local and university museums, as well as more broadly within national museums (see Bud on the UK, and Chelnick on the US, in this volume). And there remains the possibility that as new forms of public and academic discourse develop, and new technologies of presentation emerge, historical collections might speak to the future as well as the past: to be active shapers of public discourse about medicine and its place in modern society (see Söderqvist and Pedersen in this volume), or even to transcend physicality, when operating online in a digital cultural space (see Ebenstein in this volume).

The story of Henry Wellcome, and of his two medical museums – one avowedly historical, the other scientific – and their evolution into Wellcome Collection encapsulates many of these issues, and provides an illuminating lens through which we can look both back and forward. A child of the newly settled American plains, the pharmacist, entrepreneur, philanthropist and collector Henry Solomon Wellcome (Figure 2) was the reverse of those who travelled west in order to escape the burden of history. Ambition instead drew him east, to New York in 1874, and then in 1880 to England where he co-founded a pharmaceutical company with fellow American Silas Burroughs. Burroughs Wellcome & Co.'s success derived from a combination of technological innovation and an early awareness of the power of marketing, exemplified in the coinage of the word 'Tabloid' – a name combining the 'tablet' and 'alkaloid' – which became synonymous with the company's products (Figure 3).

The company's success provided Wellcome with the resources to indulge his eclectic range of interests: tropical medicine, archaeology, world travel, philanthropy, and aerial photography. But foremost among these was a passion for history and for the accumulation of historical artefacts of every kind, from manuscripts to mummies, amulets to amputation saws and scalpels to shop signs (Figures 4 and 5).[1] Wellcome's collecting became a grand project to demonstrate 'by means of objects [...] every notable step in the evolution and progress from the first germ of life up to the fully developed man of today.'[2] His project was by his own admission both anthropological and medical in nature and focus: 'My interest in anthropology, [he explained] came before the medical, but still they have both continued on parallel lines or have been merged.' United, he claimed, they demonstrated a fundamental concern with 'the

FIGURE 5
Mummified male body from Peru, 13th or 14th century, from Henry Wellcome's collections.
Image: Wellcome Library, London.

preservation of health and life [which had, he argued, always] been uppermost in the minds of living beings.'[3]

By the time of his death in 1936, Wellcome's obsessive collecting – much of it performed by agents acting on his behalf – had resulted in the accumulation of over a million items. Perhaps because of his quasi-pathological compulsion to acquire, Wellcome never succeeded in properly translating his collections into a public museum. The Wellcome Historical Medical Museum on Wigmore Street in London was opened in 1913 but although it possessed (in the words of one correspondent) 'more curious things per cubic foot than any other museum in London', Wellcome was reluctant to promote the museum until his collection was complete.[4] By setting himself this impossible goal he never succeeded in creating his planned 'Museum of Man', despite a move to new and larger premises on Euston Road in 1932. Here it was united with the Wellcome Museum of Medical Science (Figure 6), a teaching museum founded in 1914 as part of

the Wellcome Bureau of Scientific Research. Initially focusing on tropical diseases and hygiene, and later expanded to encompass all spheres of medical science, the Museum of Medical Science was avowedly ahistorical in its approach. 'Progress is the essence of its existence', asserted its curator Sidney Daukes.[5]

With Wellcome's death his collections and his wealth (in the form of the shareholding of the company) passed into the care of an eponymous charitable foundation charged with perpetuating his vision. Today the Wellcome Trust is one of the world's largest medical charities, spending in the region of £600 million per year in the UK and internationally to support research to improve human and animal health. Unusually for a medical research charity (though less remarkable in the context of its founder's interests), the Wellcome Trust also funds a range of activities that seek to broaden engagement with medical science beyond the narrow confines of the laboratory or clinic. These range from support for academic research in the history of medicine and medical humanities, and grant schemes for artists and performers, through to funding for innovative education and broadcast projects. Yet the Trust was not always so handsomely endowed, nor so expansive in its interests.

FIGURE 9
'Neural tube closing dress', from the
Primitive Streak SciArt project, a
collaboration between designer Helen
Storey and biologist Kate Storey, 1997.
Image: Justine/Wellcome Images.

In the decades after World War II, the faltering fortunes of the company probably encouraged the closure of the Wellcome Historical Medical Museum and the dispersal of great swathes of Henry Wellcome's historical collections (Figure 7), which culminated in the late 1970s with the decision to transfer the remaining 100,000 or so 'medical' artefacts to London's Science Museum on permanent loan (see Bud in this volume). While the extensive library, including a vast collection of paintings, prints and drawings, remained part of the Trust, and the Wellcome Museum of Medical Science continued to enthral medical and the occasional non-medical visitors with its displays of items such as giant tapeworms and 'mossy feet' (massive swelling caused by podoconiosis), little tangible evidence remained within the Trust of Henry Wellcome's historical medical museum scheme.

Arguably it was the relocation of the historical object collections (allied to the growing financial muscle of the Trust) that created the space – physically and intellectually – in which to fulfil Wellcome's ambition of exploring health and wellbeing in its broadest cultural sense. From the early 1990s, a budding programme of changing exhibitions at the Trust drew on the material housed at the Science Museum and in the Wellcome Library to explore themes that, while grounded in the history of medicine, increasingly took a more wide-ranging approach to their subjects (Figure 8). In 1996 the Trust instituted the SciArt project, providing funding for experimental arts projects that explored scientific ideas (Figure 9). Although the Wellcome Trust was an active supporter of new science centres elsewhere in the UK, by the early years of the twenty-first century there was increasing support within the Trust for medically themed exhibitions grounded in the arts and humanities. And in 2007 Wellcome Collection opened as a new cultural venue on Euston Road, dedicated to exploring the intersection of medicine, life and art – a vision derived from Henry Wellcome's interest in the anthropology of medicine, albeit one now unashamedly aimed at the 'curious public' (Figures 10 and. 11).[6]

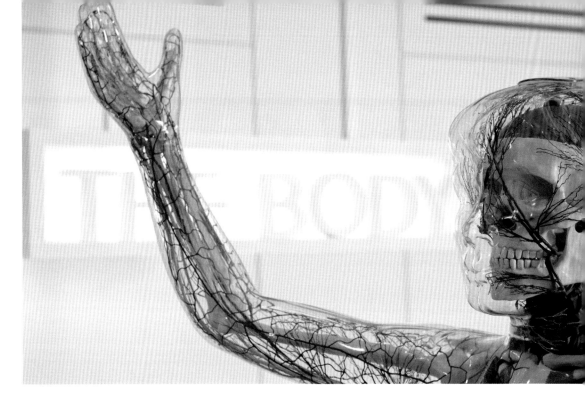

FIGURE 10
Transparent Woman from *Medicine Now*, one of two permanent galleries at Wellcome Collection.
Image: Rama Knight/Wellcome Images

As its name suggests, Wellcome Collection is an assemblage, or rather a series of assemblages: of 'things', most of them originally accumulated by Henry Wellcome; of activities, most notably a varied programme of exhibitions and events; and of spaces, including the Wellcome Library, a conference centre, and other social spaces. But it is also a collection of, and crucible for, ideas. Using its programmes to span disciplines, professions, institutions and belief systems, Wellcome Collection is rooted in the conviction that our understanding of health and medicine demands exploration of more than just the work of scientists and doctors. It also crucially requires exploration of – as Henry Wellcome would put it – 'life itself'. Thus Wellcome Collection draws upon, and reinvents, Wellcome's vision, as well as the much longer-term practices of medical collecting and display that are illustrated in this book.

As a cross between museum, gallery and event centre, Wellcome Collection serves as a platform for curiosity-driven investigations: a place to think out loud and in public. Less concerned simply to parade what is already known, and to use exhibitions to present the products of research to new audiences, it instead seeks to engender new ideas and create

FIGURE 11
Masks on display in *Medicine Man*,
a permanent exhibition about
Henry Wellcome's collection.
Image: Wellcome Library, London.

new opportunities for understanding medicine by putting it 'on show'. Aimed primarily at all-adult (14 years and older), culturally engaged visitors, and working towards as broad an audience as possible, the profile of Wellcome Collection's visitors is similar to that of many London arts venues – more female than male, predominantly in the 20–35 age group and mainly from London and the home counties. One of the very successful events staged at Wellcome Collection in its opening season was based on the idea of giving this type of audience an opportunity to witness surgery as it actually happened, an activity that was linked to the first temporary exhibition on the heart (Figure 12). So on an evening in summer 2007, an audience of over 200 sat in Wellcome Collection's auditorium and watched, via a two-way live video link, an open-heart operation happening at Papworth Hospital in Cambridge. Not only given the opportunity to observe and learn about this extraordinary, though now routine, audacious medical accomplishment, attendees were also able to ask questions of leading heart surgeon Francis Wells as he performed a complex reconstruction of a heart valve. What remains so memorable from that evening was the intense sense of curiosity and rapt attention visible on the faces of those present, palpably caught up in the drama of life-saving surgery.

While some aspects of medical practice have been conducted within the public domain over previous centuries, whether in the form of the public 'theatre' of renaissance anatomy or the showbusiness of pharmaceutical entrepreneurs, many medical treatments of the human body – living or dead –

are now performed in spaces strictly reserved for professionals. In this context, Wellcome Collection self-consciously draws upon and actively stimulates public interest in the performance of medicine. It does so with purpose: some commentators have argued that parts of modern medicine have recently become worryingly de-personalised, and removed from the public domain.[7] If that is the case, then maybe events like 'live surgery' might just help to remind audiences that medicine is still fundamentally about real people at all levels, from patients, through clinical practitioners, all the way to researchers. This is not, however, a case of replacing the old 'inside-out' view of medical museum-making – of narratives provided by practitioners for public consumption – with an 'outside-in' perspective that privileges artistic imagination over scientific work. Instead, it is an approach that echoes the author Vladimir Nabokov's poetic observation that 'there is no science without fancy, and no art without facts'.[8] Drawing on this conviction allows Wellcome Collection to escape from the deadening cliché that medical museums or science exhibits should invariably feed information and promote intellectual understanding, while art can only properly work on the emotions. Wellcome Collection just as often champions the opposite: it promotes medical science that inspires dreams and the imagination and art that informs and teaches (Figures 13 and 14).

Wellcome Collection neither evolved nor exists in isolation. It shares its ambitions and elements of its approach with museums such as the Deutches Hygiene Museum in Dresden,

the Charité museum in Berlin and the Medical Museion in Copenhagen (see Schnalke, and Södeqvist and Pederson, in this volume); with cultural programmes such as the Serpentine Gallery's 'Park Nights' series and the Hayward Gallery's 'Wide Open School', both in London, and with innovative science centres such as the Laboratoire in Paris and the Science Gallery in Dublin. This is not an exhaustive list, and there is arguably more that is different than similar about these initiatives, but they have in common the belief that medical and scientific ideas can be explored in public through cultural projects. All seek to bend or play with the conventions that otherwise define their sectors, and champion innovation and creativity over convention. This drive to experiment – with its incumbent risk of failure – is a defining quality of science (if not necessarily always of medical practice), and it remains at the heart of Wellcome Collection's mission (Figure 15).

For all of its success, there are still challenges to face, and new opportunities to be explored. Wellcome Collection's popularity has meant that it receives almost half a million visits per year, in a venue designed (at the time, optimistically) for a fifth of that figure. While the exhibitions draw heavily on the Wellcome Library's collections, too many barriers remain between the 'curious public' and the dedicated researcher, and much of what is still held on site is largely invisible to the majority of visitors. There is too a nagging sense, derived in part from analysis of the level of repeat visits to Wellcome Collection, that there is a hitherto untapped, or rather unsated, demand for content that exists over a wider spectrum of timescales, for temporary exhibitions that last more than a few months, and which evolve rather than remain static, or for events that take place over weeks rather than hours. Developing Wellcome Collection will not therefore be a case of offering more of the same but rather offering more that is different. For all its rich tradition (drawing on a reinvigorated approach to an important historical collection and an ongoing concern with the deep past of museum history),

FIGURE 14 (OPPOSITE)
Glass sculpture of HIV virus
by Luke Jerram, 2004.
Image: Luke Jerram/Wellcome Images

perhaps the designation 'medical museum' provides too narrow a scope for such endeavour. For if the past, as outlined in the preceding chapters of this volume, offers any lessons, it is that the futures of medical museums need not – perhaps should not – be defined by their histories alone. The medical museum is dead. Long live the medical museum!

NOTES

1. See Frances Larson, *An infinity of things: How Sir Henry Wellcome Collected the World* (Oxford: Oxford University Press, 2009).

2. Henry Wellcome to Louis Malcolm, 31 August 1926, quoted in Ghislaine Skinner, 'Sir Henry Wellcome's Museum for the Science of History', *Medical History*, 30 (1986), 383–418 (p. 399).

3. Royal Commission on National Museums and Galleries, *Oral Evidence, Memoranda and Appendices to the Final Report* (London: HMSO, 1929), p. 108.

4. *The Amateur Photographer*, 8 April 1931, quoted in *Larson, An Infinity of Things*, p. 149.

5. Sidney Daukes, *The Medical Museum: Modern Development, Organisation and Technical Methods Based on a New System of Visual Teaching* (London: The Wellcome Foundation Ltd, 1929), p. 26.

6. See Marek Kohn, *Wellcome Collection: A Guide for the Incurably Curious* (London: Wellcome Collection, 2012).

7. See for example Ronald A Carson, 'Engaged Humanities: Moral Work in the Precincts of Medicine', *Perspectives in Biology and Medicine*, 50 (2007), 321–333.

8. Vladimir Nabokov, *Strong Opinions* (London: Weidenfield & Nicholson, 1974), p. 79.

FIGURE 15 (BELOW)
Raw meat and offal for visitors to handle, part of the Materials Library's *Flesh* event at Wellcome Collection in 2007.
Image: Wellcome Library, London.

Notes on contributors

Eva Åhrén is author of *Death, Modernity, and the Body: Sweden 1870–1940* (2009). Currently researching early microbiology at the National Institutes of Health, Bethesda, Maryland, her research has mainly focused on the roles of museums, specimens and other visualisations in modern anatomical science.

Samuel JMM Alberti is Director of Museums and Archives at the Royal College of Surgeons of England, which includes the renowned Hunterian Museum. A historian of museums, he has published on Victorian pathology, zoological specimens, and the Manchester Museum.

Ken Arnold directs the public programmes at Wellcome Collection, where the human condition is explored through the connections between medicine, art and life. He regularly writes and lectures on museums and on contemporary interactions between the arts and sciences.

Robert Bud is Keeper of Science and Medicine at The Science Museum, London. His books include *The Uses of Life: A History of Biotechnology*, *Manifesting Medicine*, and *Penicillin: Triumph and Tragedy*. He also led the *Brought to Life* digitisation project.

Simon Chaplin runs the Wellcome Library, and was previously Director of Museums at the Royal College of Surgeons of England. His research interests include the histories of dissection and display. He is a Trustee of the Florence Nightingale Museum.

Judy M Chelnik is an Associate Curator in the Division of Medicine and Science at the Smithsonian Institution's National Museum of American History (NMAH) in Washington DC. She is a member of the NMAH Collections Committee and is active in several national and international professional organisations.

Flurin Condrau teaches the history of medicine at the University of Zurich, Switzerland, a position previously held by Erwin H Ackerknecht. His main interests are in the histories of infectious diseases, hospital infection and medical patients.

Joanna Ebenstein is a New York-based artist and independent researcher. She runs the Morbid Anatomy Library – which makes available to the public her collection of anatomically themed books, research materials, curiosities, artworks, and artifacts – and the Morbid Anatomy blog.

James M Edmondson is Chief Curator of the Dittrick Medical History Center (Case Western Reserve University). He has curated exhibitions on medical history, authored *American Surgical Instruments* (1997) and co-authored *Dissection: Photographs of a Rite of Passage in American Medicine* (2009).

Elizabeth Hallam is a Senior Research Fellow in the Department of Anthropology, University of Aberdeen, and a Research Associate in the School of Anthropology and Museum Ethnography, University of Oxford. Her publications focus on the body, death, material culture, museums and anatomy.

Marieke Hendriksen is a postdoctoral research fellow at the University of Groningen. Her PhD dissertation at Leiden University (2012) dealt with the role of sensory perception, and notions of elegance and perfection in the creation of the eighteenth-century Leiden anatomical collections.

Chris Henry is the Director of Heritage at Surgeons' Hall Museum, at the Royal College of Surgeons of Edinburgh. Previously he was Director of the Museum of Scottish Lighthouses, and Keeper of Collections at the Royal Research Ship *Discovery* in Dundee.

Robert D Hicks is the Director of the Mütter Museum and Historical Medical Library of The College of Physicians of Philadelphia. For over three decades he has worked with exhibits and educational programming at museums and historic sites.

Heike Huistra is a Postdoctoral Researcher at Utrecht University, where she works on Dutch health care, 1890 to 1990. Her doctoral thesis (2012), completed at Leiden University, discusses how non-medical audiences disappeared from the nineteenth-century Leiden anatomical collections.

Rina Knoeff is Senior Researcher at the University of Groningen. She works on the history of the body in the Enlightenment. She recently completed a project on the Leiden University Anatomical Collections, which she analysed from the visitor's point of view.

Anna Maerker is a Senior Lecturer in History of Medicine at King's College London. Her work explores the relationship between experts and the public, and the material culture of medicine. She frequently contributes to museum projects such as the Science Museum's website *Brought to Life*.

Bente Vinge Pedersen has an MA in History and Danish Literature and Language. She joined the Copenhagen Medical Museion in 2006 and is now Senior Curator with responsibility for coordinating exhibitions and public outreach. She has recently been the lead curator of *Obesity: What's The Problem?*

Michael Rhode was Chief Archivist of the National Museum of Health and Medicine (AKA the US Army Medical Museum) from 1989 to 2011. He is currently the Archivist/Curator of the US Navy's Bureau of Medicine and Surgery's Office of Medical History.

Thomas Schnalke is a trained physician and medical historian. His books include *Diseases in Wax* (1995), and *Medizin im Brief* (1997) on eighteenth-century urban physicians. In 2000 he became Professor for Medical History and Medical Museology at the Berlin Charité, and Director of the Berlin Museum for Medical History at the Charité.

Thomas Söderqvist is Professor in History of Medicine and Director of Medical Museion, University of Copenhagen. Drawing on more than thirty years of research experience in the history of twentieth-century biosciences, he spends much of his time discussing museums and science studies on Twitter (@museionist).

Glossary

Anthropometry is the study of human beings by measuring features of their bodies.

Auscultation is the medical practice of listening to sounds inside the body, usually by using a stethoscope.

Bacteriology is the study of bacteria, the most numerous of all living organisms on Earth.

Cardiology is the medical study of the heart and its diseases.

Comparative anatomy is the study of differences and similarities in the anatomy (or physical structure) of animals (including humans) and plants.

Craniology is the study of the cranium (the part of the skull excluding the lower jaw) in terms of shape and size.

Dermatology is the medical study of skin diseases.

Electrocardiography interprets the electrical activity of the heart to monitor, and produce readings of, the rhythm of heartbeats.

Endoscopy is the medical practice of looking into the body with an endoscope (an instrument comprising a fine tube with a light and lens at the end).

Epidemiology is the study of the prevalence, spread and effects of disease in populations.

Gynaecology is the field of medicine concerned with diseases of female reproductive organs.

Histology is the study of anatomy in animals (including humans) and plants which is visible with a microscope rather than the naked eye.

Interactive exhibit is a museum exhibit that invites museum visitors to interact with it – for example, through touch and sound, rather than just looking.

Maxillofacial surgery is the branch surgery concerned with the mouth, jaw, face and neck.

Medical humanities are studies that draw on humanities subjects (e.g. literature studies, philosophy and history), the social sciences (e.g. anthropology and psychology) and the arts to enhance understanding of medical practice, heath and illness.

Microtome is an instrument used to cut extremely fine slices or sections, of human tissue, usually so that they can be observed with a microscope.

Mitral valve is a valve in the heart between the left atrium and left ventricle that helps to control the flow of blood.

Morbid anatomy (see pathology)

Moulage is a cast of the surface of the skin.

Numismatics is the study and collection of currency, including coins and paper money.

Obstetrics is the field of medicine concerned with the care of women during pregnancy, childbirth and the postnatal phase.

Odontology is the study of teeth, including their development and diseases.

Ophthalmoscope is an instrument for examining the interior of the eye.

Osteoarchaeology is the study of bones from archaeological sites.

Otoscope is an instrument for the medical examination of the ear canal and middle ear cavity.

Pathology is the study and diagnosis of disease.

Quack remedy is a remedy offered by an unqualified or supposedly fake medical practitioner.

Sci-art refers to experimental projects involving scientists and artists in collaborations that explore science through art, thereby providing innovative perspectives on both areas.

Sphygmomanometer is a device for measuring blood pressure.

Stereolithography is a 3D printing technology for producing models and components.

Stereoscopic photograph is composed of two photographs taken from slightly different angles that appear three dimensional when viewed together, usually with a stereoscope.

String galvanometer is an instrument that detects and records the heart's electrical currents.

Teratology is the study of (what is defined as) abnormal physical development in animals (including humans) and plants.

Topographical anatomy is the study of anatomy in regions, such as the thorax or abdomen, focusing in the relations between structures (or parts) in those regions.

Urology is the medical study of those organs which deal with the production, storage and passage of urine in women and men. It also includes the medical study of men's reproductive organs.

Ventricular assist device is a battery-operated mechanical device that helps failing human hearts to function.

Further reading

Åhrén, Eva, Death, *Modernity, and the Body: Sweden 1870–1940*, translated by Daniel W Olson (Rochester, NY: University of Rochester Press, 2009).

Alberti, Samuel JMM, *Morbid Curiosities: Medical Museums in Nineteenth-Century Britain* (Oxford: Oxford University Press, 2011).

Arnold, Ken, *Cabinets for the Curious: Looking Back at Early English Museums* (Aldershot: Ashgate, 2006).

Bud, Robert, Bernard Finn and Helmuth Trischler, eds, *Manifesting Medicine*, 2nd edn (London: Science Museum, 2004).

Chaplin, Simon, 'John Hunter and The "Museum Oeconomy", 1750–1800' (PhD thesis, King's College London, 2009).

Cooke, Robin A, ed., *Scientific Medicine in the Twentieth Century: A Commemoration of 100 Years of the International Association of Medical Museums* (Augusta: USCAP, 2006).

Doel, Ronald E, and Thomas Söderqvist, eds, *The Historiography of Contemporary Science Technology, and Medicine: Writing Recent Science* (London: Routledge, 2006).

Daston, Lorraine, and Katharine Park, *Wonders and the Order of Nature, 1150–1750* (New York: Zone, 1998).

Edmonson, James M, *American Surgical Instruments: An Illustrated History of their Manufacture and a Directory of Instrument Makers to 1900* (San Francisco: Norman, 1997).

Ellis, Harold, *The Cambridge Illustrated History of Surgery*, 2nd edn (Cambridge: Cambridge University Press, 2009).

Ferber, Sarah, and Sally Wilde, eds, *The Body Divided: Human Beings and Human 'Material' in Modern Medical History* (Farnham: Ashgate, 2012).

Fforde, Cressida, *Collecting the Dead: Archaeology and the Reburial Issue* (London: Duckworth, 2004).

Hallam, Elizabeth, *Anatomy Museum: Death and the Body Displayed* (London: Reaktion, forthcoming 2014).

Herle, Anita, Mark Elliott and Rebecca Empson, *Assembling Bodies: Art Science, and Imagination* (Cambridge: Museum of Archaeology and Anthropology, University of Cambridge, 2009).

Kemp, Dawn and Sara Barnes, *Surgeons' Hall: A Museum Anthology* (Edinburgh: The Royal College of Surgeons of Edinburgh, 2009).

Kemp, Martin and Marina Wallace, *Spectacular Bodies: The Art and Science of the Human Body from Leonardo to Now* (Berkeley: University of California Press, 2000).

Keppie, Lawrence, *William Hunter and the Hunterian Museum in Glasgow, 1807–2007* (Edinburgh: Edinburgh University Press, 2007).

Kirkup, John, *The Evolution of Surgical Instruments: An Illustrated History from Ancient Times to the Twentieth Century* (Novato, Calif.: Historyofscience.com, 2006).

Larson, Frances, *Henry Wellcome: A Life in Pieces* (Oxford: Oxford University Press, 2009).

MacDonald, Helen, *Possessing the Dead: The Artful Science of Anatomy* (Melbourne: Melbourne University Publishing 2011).

Macdonald, Sharon, *Behind the Scenes at the Science Museum* (Oxford: Berg, 2002).

Macgregor, Arthur, *Curiosity and Enlightenment: Collectors and Collections from the Sixteenth to the Nineteenth Century* (New Haven: Yale University Press, 2007).

Maerker, Anna Katharina, *Model Experts: Wax Anatomies and Enlightenment in Florence and Vienna, 1775–1815* (Manchester: Manchester University Press, 2011).

Patrizio, Andrew and Dawn Kemp, eds, *Anatomy Acts: How We Come to Know Ourselves* (Edinburgh: Birlinn, 2006).

Richardson, Ruth, *Death, Dissection and the Destitute*, 2nd edn (London: Phoenix, 2001).

Sappol, Michael, *Hidden Treasure: The National Library of Medicine* (New York: Blast Books, 2012).

Schnalke, Thomas, *Diseases in Wax: The History of the Medical Moulage*, translated by Kathy Spatschek (Chicago: Quintessence, 1995).

Stephens, Elizabeth, *Anatomy as Spectacle: Public Exhibitions of the Body from 1700 to the Present* (Liverpool: Liverpool University Press, 2011).

Weir, Sue, *Weir's Guide to Medical Museums in Britain*, 2nd edn (London, Royal Society of Medicine, 1996).

Index

Page numbers in grey refer to illustrations.